ON·SITE
GUIDE

TO THE
16TH EDITION WIRING REGULATIONS

Published by: The Institution of Electrical Engineers,
Savoy Place, London,
United Kingdom, WC2R 0BL.

ISBN 0 85296 534 6

Printed in England by G&B Litho Limited, London.
Typeset by Apek Typesetters, Nailsea, Bristol.

CONTENTS

PREFACE

The On-Site Guide is one of a number of publications prepared by the Wiring Regulations Committee of the Institution of Electrical Engineers to expand and clarify some aspects of the Sixteenth Edition Wiring Regulations.

The scope generally follows that of the Regulations and this Guide is intended to stand alone. It includes material not included in the Sixteenth Edition but which was included in earlier issues, provides background to the intentions of the Regulations, and gives other sources of information.

Electrical installations in the United Kingdom which comply with the IEE Wiring Regulations should also comply with the Statutory Regulations such as the Electricity at Work Regulations 1989. It cannot be guaranteed that the Wiring Regulations comply with all relevant Regulations and it is stressed that it is essential to establish what statutory and other Regulations apply and to install accordingly. For example an installation in Licensed Premises may have requirements different from or additional to the Wiring Regulations which will take precedence over the Wiring Regulations.

INTRODUCTION

This Guide is concerned with limited application of the Regulations in accordance with *1.1 Scope.*

The Wiring Regulations and the On-Site Guide are not design guides, although the information in this Guide is intended to reduce the need for detailed calculations. It is essential to prepare a full specification prior to commencement or alteration of an electrical installation and to provide an operational manual to the user on completion.

The specification should set out the detailed design and provide sufficient information to enable competent persons to carry out the installation and to commission it. The specification must include a description of how the system is to operate and all of the design and operational parameters.

The specification must provide for all the commissioning procedures that will be required and for the production of any operational manual.

It must be noted that it is a matter of contract as to which person or organisation is responsible for the production of the parts of the design, specification and any operational manual.

The persons or organisations who may be concerned in the preparation of the specification include:

The Designer(s)
The Installer(s)
The Supplier of Electrical Power
The Installation Owner and/or User
The Architect
The Fire Prevention Officer
All Regulatory Authorities
Any Licensing Authority
The Health and Safety Executive

In producing the specification advice should be sought from the installation owner and/or user as to the intended use. Often, such as in a speculative building, the detailed intended use is unknown. In those circumstances the specification and/or the operational manual must set out the basis of use for which the installation is suitable.

Any unusual or abnormal operating conditions should be identified.

The operational manual must include a description of how the system as installed is to operate and all commissioning records. The manual should also include leaflets for all items of switchgear, luminaires, accessories, etc. and any special instructions that may be needed. Preparation guidance is given in BS 4884, BS 4940 and Section 6 of the Health and Safety at Work Act 1974 (HSW Act).

In conformance with the convention adopted in the 16th Edition of the IEE Wiring Regulations, thoughout this Guide the term 'live part' is used to refer to a conductor or conductive part intended to be energised in normal use, including a neutral conductor. For convenience in use, and in accordance with current UK manufacturing practise the terminals of electrical equipment shown in Figs. 10.1 to 10.6 have been identified by the letters L, N and E.

NOTES

ON-SITE GUIDE

1. INTRODUCTION

1.1 Scope

This Guide is for competent electricians. It covers the following installations:

(a) Domestic installations generally, including off-peak supplies, and supplies to associated garages, out-buildings and the like.

(b) Industrial and Commercial single-and three-phase installations where the distribution board(s) is located at or near the supplier's cut-out.

Note: Special Installations or Locations (Part 6 of the 16th Edition of the IEE Wiring Regulations) are excluded from this Guide.
Bathrooms, shower cubicles and temporary buildings are included.

This Guide is restricted to installations:

(i) at a supply frequency of 50 Hertz.

(ii) at a nominal single-phase voltage of 240 volts a.c. single-phase and 240/415 volts a.c. three-phase (in Northern Ireland 230 volts a.c. and 400 volts a.c. apply).

(iii) fed through a supplier's fusible cut-out having a fuse or fuses to BS 1361 Part 2 or BS 88 Part 2 or Part 6 rated at 100 A or less.

(iv) with a maximum value of the earth fault loop impedance outside the consumer's installation as follows:

Earth return via sheath (TN-S system) : 0.8 ohm

Earth return via combined neutral and earth conductor (TN-C-S system): 0.35 ohm maximum

TT systems: 21 ohms excluding consumer's earth electrode

This Guide removes the need for detailed calculations and it also contains information which may be required in general installation work, e.g. conduit and trunking capacities, bending radii of cables etc.

This Guide introduces the use of conventional circuits, which are discussed in Part 7.

Work done to the advice in this Guide will comply with the 16th Edition of the IEE Wiring Regulations. Because of simplification this Guide may not give the most economical result.

This Guide is not a replacement for the 16th Edition of the IEE Wiring Regulations, which should always be consulted in case of doubt. Further information is available in the series of Guidance Notes published by the Institution.

1.2 Basic Information Required

Before starting work the electrician should obtain the following information from the supplier:

(i) the number of phases to be provided.

(ii) the supplier's requirement for cross-section and length of meter tails.

(iii) the maximum prospective short-circuit current (p.s.c.c.) at the supply terminals.

(iv) the maximum earth loop impedance (Z_e) of the earth fault path outside the consumer's installation.

(v) the type and rating of the supplier's fusible cut-out or protective device nearest to the supply terminals.

(vi) the supplier's requirement regarding the size of main equipotential bonding.

2. THE SERVICE POSITION

2.1 General Layout of Equipment

The general layout of the equipment at the service position is shown in Figs. 1 and 2.

2.2 Function of Components:

(i) *Supplier's Cut-out*

This will protect the consumer's installation, up to the consumer's main switch, from fault current. It will be sealed by the supplier to prevent the fuse being withdrawn by unauthorised persons. When the meter tails and consumer unit are installed in accordance with the advice of the Regional Electricity Company the supplier's cut-out may be assumed to provide fault current protection up to the consumer's main switch.

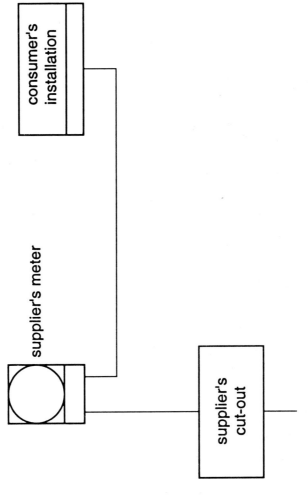

Fig. 1: Layout when the supplier does not provide a main switch

Note: Earthing arrangements have been omitted for clarity. Tails between the meter and the consumer's installation are owned by the consumer.

(ii) *Supplier's Meter*

This will be sealed by the supplier to prevent interference by unauthorised persons.

(iii) *Meter Tails*

These are part of the consumer's installation. They should be insulated and sheathed or insulated and enclosed in insulated conduit or trunking.

Polarity should be indicated by the colour of the insulation and the minimum cable size should be 25 mm^2. The supplier may specify the maximum length and the minimum cross-section (see 1.2(ii)).

Where the meter tails are protected against fault current by the supplier's cut-out the method of installation, maximum length and minimum cross-section must comply with advice provided by the supplier.

(iv) *Supplier's Switch*

Some suppliers may provide and install a suitable switch between the meter and the consumer unit. This permits supply to the installation to be interrupted without withdrawing the supplier's fuse in the cut-out.

(v) *Consumer's Installation*

This contains a main switch (which may be a residual current device (r.c.d.)) and fuses or miniature circuit breakers (m.c.bs.) and r.c.ds. for the protection of each final circuit incorporated in a consumer unit. Alternatively, a separate main switch and a fuseboard or m.c.b. board may be provided.

3. PROTECTION

3.1 Types of Protective Device(s)

The consumer unit (or distribution board) contains devices for the protection of the final circuits, against:

(i) overload.
(ii) short-circuit.
(iii) earth fault.

Functions (i) and (ii) are carried out usually by one device, a fuse or m.c.b.

Function (iii) may be carried out by the fuse or m.c.b. provided for functions (i) and (ii), or by an r.c.d.

4

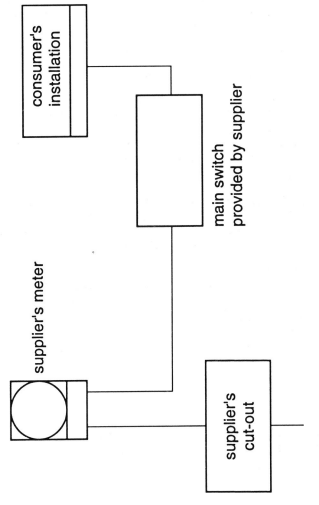

Fig. 2: Layout when the supplier does provide a main switch

Note: Earthing connections have been omitted for clarity. Tails between the meter and the consumer's installation are owned by the consumer.

3.2 Overload Protection

Overload protection is given by the following devices:

Fuses to BS 88 Part 2 or Part 6; BS 1361 and BS 3036;
m.c.bs. to BS 3871 Types 1, 2, 3, B and C.

3.3 Short-circuit Protection

When a consumer unit to BS 5486, or a fuse-board having
fuselinks to BS 88 Part 2 or Part 6 or BS 1361 is used, then
short-circuit protection will be given by the overload
protective device.

For other protective devices the breaking capacity must be
adequate for the prospective short-circuit current at that
point.

3.4 Protection Against Electric Shock

(i) *Direct Contact*
Electrical insulation and enclosures and barriers give
protection against direct contact. Non-sheathed insulated
conductors must be protected by conduit or trunking or
be within a suitable enclosure. A 30 mA r.c.d. may be
provided to give supplementary protection against direct
contact, but must not be relied upon for primary
protection.

(ii) *Indirect Contact*
Protection against indirect contact is obtained by limiting
the magnitude and duration of the fault current. This
can be done by the:

(a) co-ordination of protective devices and circuit
impedances, or

(b) use of r.c.ds. to limit the disconnection time, or

(c) use of Class II equipment or equivalent insulation.

3.5 Disconnection Times

3.5.1 Conventional Circuits

For the conventional circuits given in Part 7 below, the
correct disconnection time in second(s) (0.4 s or 5 s) is
obtained by using the protective devices and related
maximum circuit lengths in Table 7.1.

6

3.5.2 Special Circuits

A disconnection time of not more than 0.4 s is required for final circuits supplying:

(i) portable equipment intended to be moved by hand while in use.

(ii) hand-held metal-cased equipment requiring an earth, and supplied directly or through a socket-outlet.

(iii) fixed equipment outside the equipotential zone.

(iv) fixed equipment in bathrooms etc.

3.6 Residual Current Devices

3.6.1 Protection by an r.c.d.

There are a number of instances where an installation is required to incorporate one or more r.c.ds. These instances include:

(i) where the earth fault loop impedance is too high to provide the required disconnection time.

(ii) on socket-outlet circuits in TT systems.

(iii) on a socket-outlet likely to feed portable equipment used outdoors.

3.6.2 Siting the r.c.d.

Whilst some of these requirements can be met by individual socket-outlets incorporating r.c.ds., there can be advantages in protecting the whole of the circuit containing the relevant socket(s) by a single r.c.d.

The use of r.c.ds. in a consumer unit needs careful thought. There are four options:

(i) to have an r.c.d. as the main switch. This may be seen as the most cost-effective option, but the effect of the operation of the r.c.d. in controlling the supply to the installation should be carefully assessed.

(ii) to have the r.c.d. control part of the consumer unit, e.g., by use of a split-load unit.

(iii) to have a number of r.c.ds. control individual circuits, e.g., by the use of combined m.c.b./r.c.d. devices.

(iv) to combine (ii) or (iii) with (i). Care should be taken to ensure that r.c.ds. in series discriminate by making the r.c.d. used as the main switch a time-delayed device.

4. BONDING AND EARTHING

4.1 Main Equipotential Bonding Conductors (Fig. 3, 4 or 5)

Main equipotential bonding conductors are required to connect the following metallic parts to the main earthing terminal:

(i) main water pipes.

(ii) gas installation pipes.

(iii) other service pipes (including bulk oil and gas pipes) and ducting, particular attention being paid to bonding across meters.

(iv) central heating and air conditioning systems.

(v) exposed metallic structural parts of the building.

(vi) lightning protection systems.

The minimum equipotential conductor size is half the size of the main earthing conductor. For the installations covered by this Guide, the main earthing conductor is 16 mm² so that the minimum size of the main bonding conductor is 10 mm². This size will also satisfy the requirements of the Electricity Supply Regulations for a pme supply (TN-C-S) where the size of the supply neutral conductor is not more than 35 mm².

Note that:

(vii) only copper conductors are to be used; copper covered aluminium conductors are not to be used.

(viii) bonding connections to incoming metallic services should be as near as possible to the point of entry of the services to the premises, but on the consumer's side of any insulating section.

(ix) the connection to the Gas Service should be within 600 mm of the gas meter and must be on the consumer's side before any branch pipework and after any insulating section in the service. The connection must be made to hard pipe, not to soft or flexible meter connections.

(x) the connection must be made using clips which will not cause electrolytic action at the point of contact.

4.2 Earth Electrode (Fig. 5)

This is connected to the main earthing terminal by the earthing conductor and provides part of the earth return for a TT installation.

The recommended maximum value of the earth fault loop impedance is 220 ohms.

4.3 Types of Electrode

The following types of earth electrodes are recognised:

(i)   earth rods or pipes.

(ii)   earth tapes or wires.

(iii)   earth plates.

(iv)   underground structural metal work embedded in foundations.

(v)   welded metal reinforcements of concrete embedded in the earth (excluding pre-stressed concrete).

(vi)   lead sheaths and metal coverings of cables (see Note below).

Note: Where the lead sheath of a cable is used as an earth electrode the following additional conditions shall apply:

(vii)   the sheath or covering shall be in effective contact with earth.

(viii) the consent of the owner of the cable shall be obtained.

(ix)   arrangements shall exist for the owner of the electrical installation to be warned of any proposed change to the cable which might affect its suitability as an earth electrode.

4.4 Typical Earthing Arrangements for Various Types of Earthing System (Fig. 3, 4 or 5)

Note that the sizes referred to are of copper conductors related to 25 mm^2 copper supply tails from the meter.

The earthing bar is sometimes used as the main earthing terminal.

Note: For TN-S and TN-C-S installations, advice about the availability of an earth terminal and the precise arrangements for connection should be obtained from the Regional Electricity Company.

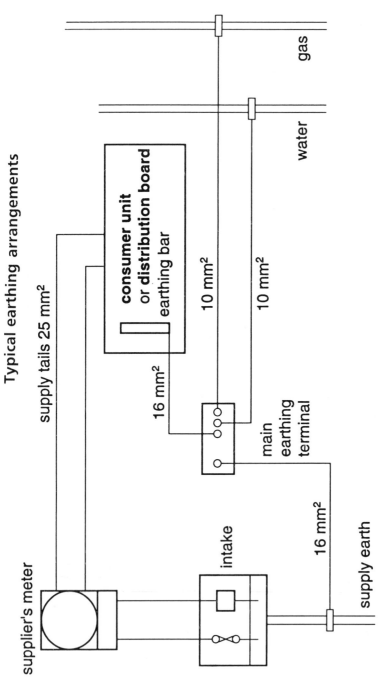

Typical earthing arrangements

supplier's meter

supply tails 25 mm²

consumer unit
or distribution board
earthing bar

gas

water

10 mm²

10 mm²

16 mm²

main
earthing
terminal

intake

16 mm²

supply earth

Fig. 3: TN-S: Earthed to armour or metallic sheath

Note: i) The single-phase arrangement is shown but the three-phase arrangement is similar.
ii) Equipotential bonding conductors may be separate (as shown) or one continuous conductor looped.

10

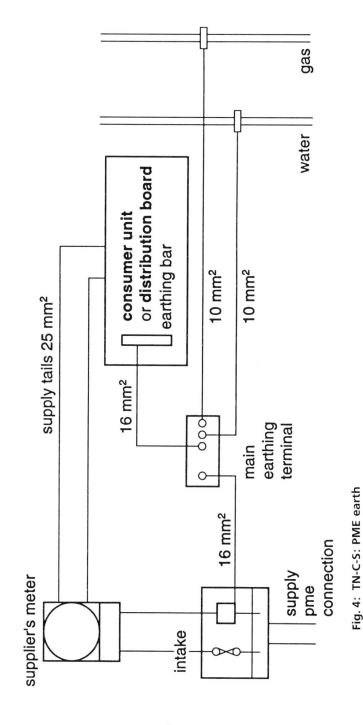

supplier's meter

supply tails 25 mm²

consumer unit or distribution board earthing bar

16 mm²

10 mm²

10 mm²

main earthing terminal

16 mm²

intake

supply pme connection

water

gas

Fig. 4: TN-C-S: PME earth

Note: i) The single-phase arrangement is shown but the three-phase arrangement is similar.
ii) Equipotential bonding conductors may be separate (as shown) or one continuous conductor looped.

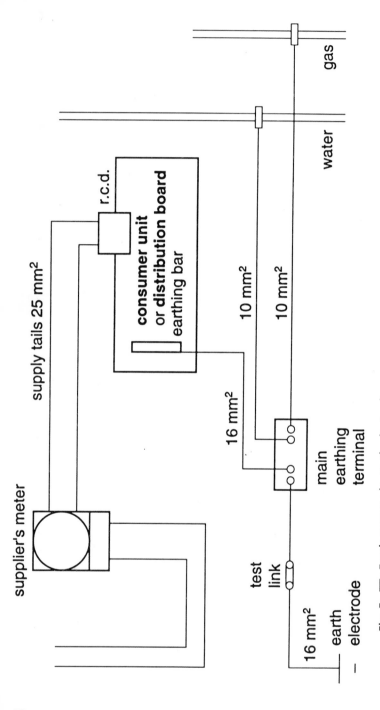

Fig. 5: TT: Earth return via earth electrode

Note: i) The single-phase arrangement is shown but the three-phase arrangement is similar.

ii) Equipotential bonding conductors may be separate (as shown) or one continuous conductor looped.

iii) See Table 54A for requirements when earthing conductor is buried in the ground.

5. ISOLATION AND SWITCHING

5.1 Isolation

A means of isolation is required to enable skilled persons to carry out work on, or near, parts which would otherwise normally be live.

A means of isolation should be provided as follows:

(i)   a main linked switch or circuit breaker should be provided as near as possible to the origin of the installation as a means of interrupting the supply on load and as a means of isolation. For single-phase supplies a double-pole device must be used regardless of the supply system.

(ii) every circuit, or group of circuits, which may have to be isolated without interrupting the supply to other circuits should be provided with an isolating device.

(iii) every motor circuit should be provided with an isolating device which will disconnect the motor and all associated equipment including any automatic circuit breaker.

Isolating devices must comply with British Standards. The position of the contacts or other means of isolation must either be externally visible or be clearly indicated. If installed remotely from the equipment to be isolated, the device must be capable of being secured in the OPEN position.

Isolators must switch all live conductors in TT systems and all phase conductors in TN-S or TN-C-S systems.

5.2 Functional Switching

A means of switching for interrupting the supply on load is required for every circuit and final circuit.

One common switch may be used to interrupt the supply to a group of circuits. Additionally, a separate switch must be provided for every circuit which, for safety reasons, has to be switched independently.

5.3 Switching Off for Mechanical Maintenance

A means of switching off for mechanical maintenance is required where mechanical maintenance may involve a risk of burns or of injury from mechanical movement, and may be required for lamp replacement.

Each device for switching off for mechanical maintenance must:

(i)   be capable of switching full load current.

(ii) be located in a readily accessible position.

(iii) be identified with a permanent label.

(iv) have either an externally visible contact gap or a clearly and reliably indicated OFF position. An indicating light should not be relied upon.

(v)   be selected and installed to prevent unintentional reclosure, such as might be caused by mechanical shock or vibration.

5.4 Emergency Switching

An emergency switch is to be provided for every part of an installation which may have to be rapidly disconnected from the supply to prevent or remove danger. Where there is a risk of electric shock the emergency switch is to disconnect all live conductors, *except* in three-phase TN-S and TN-C-S systems where the neutral need not be switched.

A means of emergency stopping is also to be provided where mechanical movement of electrically actuated equipment may give rise to danger.

An emergency switch is to be:

(i)   readily accessible from the place where the danger may occur.

(ii) marked, preferably with a red handle or push button.

(iii) capable of cutting off the full load current.

(iv) capable of being latched or restrained 'OFF'.

(v)   double-pole for single-phase systems.

A fireman's emergency switch is to be provided to disconnect supply to a high voltage installation, e.g., a neon sign, but such installations are outside the scope of this Guide.

6. LABELLING

6.1 Labels to be Provided

The following labels are to be provided on or adjacent to equipment installed in final circuits:

(i) *Unexpected presence of voltage exceeding 250 volts*

Where the voltage exceeds 250 and it would not normally be expected to be so high, a warning label giving the maximum voltage present shall be provided so that it can be seen before gaining access to live parts.

(ii) *Voltage exceeding 250 volts between simultaneously accessible equipment*

In simultaneously accessible adjacent equipment where terminals or other fixed live parts have a voltage exceeding 250 volts between them, a warning label shall be provided so that it can be seen before gaining access to live parts.

(iii) *Presence of different nominal voltages in the same equipment*

Where equipment contains different nominal voltages, e.g. both low and extra-low, a warning label stating the voltages present shall be provided so that it can be seen before gaining access to simultaneously accessible live parts.

(iv) *Connection of bonding conductors*

A permanent label durably marked with the words as follows and no smaller than the example shown in the 16th Edition of the IEE Wiring Regulations

---

SAFETY ELECTRICAL CONNECTION—DO NOT REMOVE

---

shall be fixed in a visible position at or near the point of connection of every bonding conductor to extraneous-conductive-parts and to every earthing conductor to an earth electrode or other means of earthing.

(v)   *Purpose of switchgear and control gear*

Unless there is no possibility of confusion a label indicating the purpose of switchgear and controlgear shall be fixed on or adjacent to the gear. It may be necessary to label the item controlled, as well as its controlgear.

(vi)   *Identification of isolators*

All isolating devices shall be clearly and durably marked to indicate the circuit or circuits which they isolate.

(vii)   *Isolation by more than one device*

A durable warning notice must be permanently fixed in a clearly visible position to identify the appropriate isolating devices, where equipment or an enclosure contains live parts which cannot be isolated by a single device.

(viii)   *Periodic inspection and testing*

A notice of durable material indelibly marked with the words as follows, and no smaller than the example shown in the 16th Edition of the IEE Wiring Regulations

---

IMPORTANT

This installation should be periodically inspected and tested and a report on its condition obtained, as prescribed in the Regulations for Electrical Installations issued by the Institution of Electrical Engineers.

Date of last inspection...................

Recommended date of next inspection..............

---

shall be fixed in a prominent position at the origin of every installation.

(ix) Where an installation incorporates an r.c.d. a notice with the words as follows, and no smaller than the example shown in the 16th Edition of the IEE Wiring Regulations

---

This installation, or part of it, is protected by a device which automatically switches off the supply if an earth fault develops. Test quarterly by pressing the button marked 'T' or 'Test'. The device should switch off the supply and should then be switched on to restore the supply. If the device does not switch off the supply when the button is pressed, seek expert advice.

---

shall be fixed in a prominent position at the origin of the installation.

7. CONVENTIONAL FINAL CIRCUITS

7.1 Installation of Conventional Final Circuits

Table 7.1 has been designed to enable a radial or ring conventional final circuit to be installed without calculation.

The conditions assumed are that:

(i) The installation is supplied by a TN-C-S system with a maximum earth fault loop impedance outside the installation Z_e of 0.35 ohm or by a TN-S system with a maximum Z_e of 0.8 ohm.

(ii) The final circuit is connected to a distribution board or consumer unit at the origin of the installation.

(iii) The method of installation complies with Reference Methods 1, 3 or 4 of Appendix 4 of the 16th Edition of the IEE Wiring Regulations:

(a) *Reference Method 1*
Sheathed cables clipped direct, or embedded in plaster.

(b) *Reference Method 3*
Cables run in conduit or trunking.

TABLE 7.1

Conventional Circuits

Disconnection times for m.c.bs. are taken from the 16th Edition.
A tripping time of 0.1 s or less is assumed.
For further information consult Notes on page 20, Appendix 7 and Appendix 9.

Ring Circuits

Current rating A	Cable size mm² Conductor/ c.p.c.	Protective device	Maximum length in metres			
			TN-S 0.4 s	TN-S 5 s	TN-C-S 0.4 s	TN-C-S 5 s
30	2.5/1.5	BS1361	59(*A)	N1	71	N1
		BS3036(*B) & m.c.b. Type 2	50(*A)	N1	71	N1
		m.c.b. Type 1 & B	71	N1	71	N1
		m.c.b. Type 3 & C	N2	N1	66(*A)	N1
32	2.5/1.5	BS88	43(*A)	N1	66	N1
		m.c.b. Type 1 & B	66	N1	66	N1
		m.c.b. Type 2	40(*A)	N1	66	N1
		m.c.b. 3 & C	N2	N1	59(*A)	N1
Radial circuits						
5	1.0/1.0	BS3036 & m.c.b. Type 1,2,3,B & C	43	43	43	43
5	1.5/1.0	BS3036 & m.c.b. Type 1,2,3,B & C	66	66	66	66
6	1.0/1.0	BS88 & BS3036 & m.c.b. Type 1,2,3,B & C	36	36	36	36
6	1.5/1.0	BS88 & BS3036 & m.c.b. Type 1,2,3,B & C	55	55	55	55
15	2.5/1.5	BS3036(*B) & m.c.b. Type 1,2 & B	35	35	35	35
		m.c.b. Type 3 & C	29(*A)	29(*A)	35	35
15	4.0/1.5	BS3036(*B) & m.c.b. Type 1,2 & B	58	58	58	58
		m.c.b. Type 3 & C	34(*A)	34(*A)	54(*A)	54(*A)
16	2.5/1.5	BS88 & BS 3036(*B) & m.c.b. Type 1,2 & B	33	33	33	33
		m.c.b. Type 3 & C	25(*A)	25(*A)	33	33
16	4.0/1.5	BS88 & BS3036(*B) & m.c.b. Type 1,2 & B	54	54	54	54
		m.c.b. Type 3 & C	30(*A)	30(*A)	49(*A)	49(*A)

TABLE 7.1 continued

Conventional Circuits

Disconnection times for m.c.bs. are taken from the 16th Edition.
A tripping time of 0.1 s or less is assumed.
For further information consult Notes on page 20, Appendix 7 and Appendix 9.

Ring Circuits
RADIAL

Current rating A	Cable size mm² Conductor/ c.p.c.	Protective device	Maximum length in metres			
			TN-S 0.4 s	TN-S 5 s	TN-C-S 0.4 s	TN-C-S 5 s
20	2.5/1.5	BS88, BS1361 & BS3036(*B) & m.c.b. Type 1, 2 & B	26	26	26	26
		m.c.b. Type 3 & C	14(*A)	14(*A)	26	26
20	4.0/1.5	BS88 & BS3036(*B) & m.c.b. Type 1 & B	43	43	43	43
		m.c.b. Type 2	39(*A)	39(*A)	43	43
		m.c.b. Type 3 & C	17(*A)	17(*A)	36(*A)	36(*A)
30	6.0/2.5	BS3036(*C)	23(*A)	43	43	43
		BS1361	27(*A)	43	43	43
		m.c.b. Type 1 & B	43	43	43	43
		m.c.b. Type 2	23(*A)	23(*A)	43	43
		m.c.b. Type 3 & C	N2	N2	31(*A)	31(*A)
30	10.0/4.0	BS3036	38(*A)	72	72	72
		BS1361	45(*A)	72	72	72
		m.c.b. Type 1 & B	72	72	72	72
		m.c.b. Type 2	38(*A)	38(*A)	72	72
		m.c.b. Type 3 & C	N2	N2	50(*A)	50(*A)
32	6.0/2.5	BS88	20(*A)	41	41	41
		m.c.b. Type 1 & B	41	41	41	41
		m.c.b. Type 2	18(*A)	18(*A)	41	41
		m.c.b. Type 3 & C	N2	N2	27(*A)	27(*A)
32	10.0/4.0	BS88	32(*A)	68	68	68
		m.c.b. Type 1 & B	68	68	68	68
		m.c.b. Type 2	30(*A)	30(*A)	68	68
		m.c.b. Type 3 & C	N2	N2	45(*A)	45(*A)
40	10.0/4.0	BS88	6(*A)	54	54	54
		m.c.b. Type 1	54	54	54	54
		m.c.b. Type B	45(*A)	45(*A)	54	54
		m.c.b. Type 2	6(*A)	6(*A)	54	54
		m.c.b. Type 3 & C	N2	N2	28(*A)	28(*A)

TABLE 7.1 continued

Conventional Circuits

Disconnection times for m.c.bs. are taken from the 16th Edition.
A tripping time of 0.1 s or less is assumed.
For further information consult Appendix 7 and Appendix 9.

~~Ring~~ Circuits
RADIAL

Current rating A	Cable size mm² Conductor/ c.p.c.	Protective device	Maximum length in metres			
			TN-S 0.4 s	TN-S 5 s	TN-C-S 0.4 s	TN-C-S 5 s
40	16.0/6.0	BS88	9(*A)	85	85	85
		m.c.b. Type 1	85	85	85	85
		m.c.b. Type B	68(*A)	68(*A)	85	85
		m.c.b. Type 2	9(*A)	9(*A)	85	85
		m.c.b. Type 3 & C	N2	N2	42(*A)	42(*A)
45	10.0/4.0	BS1361	N2	22(*A)	28(*A)	48
		BS3036(*C)	N2	48	29(*A)	48
		m.c.b. Type 1 & B	48	48	48	48
		m.c.b. Type 2	N2	N2	43	43
		m.c.b. Type 3 & C	N2	N2	19	19
45	16.0/6.0	BS1361	N2	34(*A)	42(*A)	76
		BS3036	N2	76	45(*A)	76
		m.c.b. Type 1 & B	76	76	76	76
		m.c.b. Type 2	N2	N2	68	68
		m.c.b. Type 3 & C	N2	N2	30	30

The following are limited other than by voltage drop:

(*A) = Length is limited by earth fault loop impedance.
(*B) = Only suitable for Reference Method 1 and 3. ·
(*C) = Only suitable for Reference Method 1.

N1 = NOT PERMISSIBLE on 0.4 s grounds
N2 = NOT PERMISSIBLE on earth loop impedance grounds.

Note: (i) Reference to BS 88 fuses is to Part 2 or Part 6.
(ii) BS 88 fuses are not available in Consumer Units, for BS 1361 use the same length as for BS 3036 fuse.

(c) *Reference Method 4*
Sheathed cables, or cables in conduit, in thermal insulation but in contact with a thermally conductive surface on one side.

(iv) The ambient temperature throughout the length of the circuit does not exceed 30°C.

20

7.2 Using the Conventional Final Circuits

7.2.1 Grouping of cables

No grouping factor has been allowed for in the conventional final circuits, however, the rating of the cables used in the 5A and 6A conventional final circuits allows for some grouping:

(i) where the circuit is protected by a BS 3036 rewireable (semi-enclosed) fuse up to 4 circuits can be grouped.

(ii) where the circuit is protected by a BS 88 or 1361 fuse, or by an m.c.b. to BS 3871, up to 6 circuits can be grouped.

7.2.2 Check list

Before installing a conventional final circuit the following questions must be answered:

(i) what is the load current and can the distribution board accommodate it?

(ii) which kind of protective device is to be used?

(iii) what is the equivalent or next larger rating of the protective device?

(iv) which type of earthing arrangement is employed?

(v) is the maximum required disconnection time 0.4 s or 5 s?

Maximum 0.4 s disconnection time is required for circuits feeding socket-outlets, fixed equipment outside the equipotential zone, fixed equipment in bathrooms.

All socket-outlets on a TT system must be protected by an r.c.d. to BS 4293.

(vi) what are the isolation and switching requirements? (See Part 5)

(vii) what labels are required? (See Part 6)

(viii) is the earth loop impedance value below the values given in 7.2.3(ii)?

7.2.3 TT systems

For TT systems the figures for TN-C-S systems, with 5 s disconnection time, may be used provided that:

(i) the circuit is controlled by an r.c.d. to BS 4293 with a rated residual operating current not exceeding 200 mA, and

(ii) the total earth fault loop impedance is verified as being less than 220 ohms, and

(iii) a device giving both overload and short-circuit protection is installed in the circuit. This may be combined with the r.c.d.

7.2.4 Choice of protective device

The choice of protective device depends upon the:

(i) circuit rating.

(ii) type of protection required.

(iii) disconnection time.

(iv) maximum earth fault loop impedance permissible.

(v) type of earthing system.

(vi) prospective short-circuit current.

7.3 Installation considerations

7.3.1 Telecommunication circuits

An adequate separation between telecommunication wiring and electric power and lighting circuits must be maintained. This is to prevent mains voltage appearing in telecommunication circuits with consequent danger to personnel. BS 6701, Part 1: 1990 recommends that the following separation be maintained:

Minimum separating distances from electricity supply cables and Telecommunications cables.

TABLE 7.3A

Minimum separation distances between external low voltages electricity supply cables operating in excess of 50 V a.c. or 120 V d.c. to earth, but not exceeding 600 V a.c. or 900 V d.c. to earth and Telecommunications cables.

Voltage to earth	Normal separation distances.	Exceptions to normal separation distances, plus conditions to exception.
Exceeding 50 V a.c. or 120 V d.c., but not exceeding 600 V a.c. or 900 V d.c.	50 mm	below this figure a non-conducting divider should be inserted between the cables.

TABLE 7.3B

Minimum separation distances between internal low voltage electricity supply cables operating in excess of 50 V a.c. or 120 V d.c. to earth, but not exceeding 600 V a.c. or 900 V d.c. to earth and Telecommunications cables.

Voltage to earth	Normal separation distances.	Exceptions to normal, separation distances, plus conditions to exception.
Exceeding 50 V a.c. or 120 V d.c., but not exceeding 600 V a.c. or 900 V d.c.	50 mm	50 mm separation need not be maintained, provided that i) The LV cables are enclosed in separate conduit which if metallic is earthed in accordance with the 16th Edition of the IEE Regulations **OR** ii) The LV cables are enclosed in separate trunking which if metallic is earthed in accordance with the 16th Edition of the IEE Regulations **OR** iii) The LV cable is of the mineral insulated type or is of armoured construction **OR** iv) The LV cables share the same tray then the normal separation should be met **OR** v) Where LV and Telecommunications cables are obliged to cross, additional insulation should be provided at the crossing point; this is not necessary if either cable is armoured.

7.3.2 Proximity to Other Systems

Electrical and all other services must be protected from any harmful mutual effects foreseen as likely under conditions of normal service.

The installation must comply with Chapter 41 and Chapter 54 regarding separation and bonding.

A particular form of harmful effect may occur when an electrical installation shares the space occupied by a hearing aid induction loop.

Under these circumstances, if phase(s) and neutral or switch feeds and switch wires are not close together, there may be interference with the induction loop.

Such a case is possible when a conventional two-way circuit is installed. This effect can be reduced by connecting as shown in Fig. 6.

8. SPECIAL LOCATIONS GIVING RISE TO INCREASED RISK OF ELECTRIC SHOCK

8.1 Bathrooms and Showers

8.1.1 These locations present a greater risk of electric shock than other (dry) locations. The basic approach should be:

(i) bond all exposed and extraneous-conductive-parts together regardless of accessibility but not deliberately to the main earthing terminal. This will prevent potential differences between them.

(ii) select a protective device that operates within 0.4 s.

8.1.2 Within the bath tub or shower basin only electrical equipment and control circuits operating at 12 volts or less shall be accessible. In these locations the 12 volts must come from a remote safety isolating transformer or equivalent source.

8.1.3 Within the reach of a person in a bath or shower basin, there should be no electrical equipment, except as described in paragraph 8.1.2, equipment to BS 3456 Part 3.9 and shaver supply unit to BS 3535. The insulating cords of cord-operated switches are allowed within reach but the switch itself should be normally inaccessible to a person in a bath or shower. Any luminaires within a horizontal distance of two and a half metres should be totally enclosed.

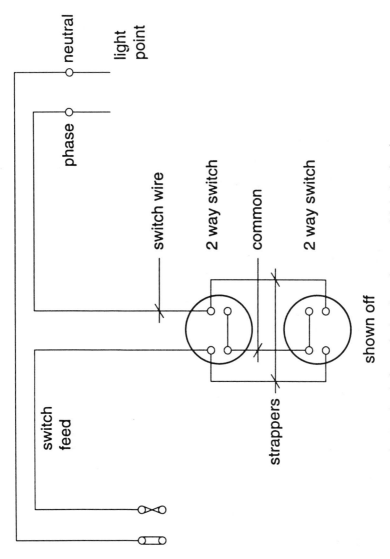

neutral

light
point

phase

switch wire

2 way switch

common

2 way switch

switch
feed

strappers

shown off

Fig. 6: Circuit for reducing interference with induction loop

25

8.1.4 All equipment in a bathroom or shower room or sauna or near to a shower should be suitable for the environment, particularly with regard to possible splashing and high humidity levels.

8.1.5 Under-floor heating installations in these areas should have an overall earthed metallic grid or the heating cable should have an earthed metallic sheath.

8.1.6 Shower cubicles in a room used for other purposes

If a shower cubicle is positioned inside another room, such as a bedroom, there should not be a socket-outlet within two and a half metres of the shower cubicle doorway.

Bayonet-type lampholders in the same area should be fitted with an insulated shield (Home Office skirt). Sockets within the room further than two and a half metres from the shower cubicle doorway should be protected by an r.c.d.

8.2 Temporary and Garden Buildings, Domestic Garages, Buildings of Lightweight Construction etc.

8.2.1 The use of a temporary building does not permit a lower standard of electrical installation. The standards of installation and maintenance need to be higher to cope with the onerous conditions. Particular attention must be paid to:

(i)   suitability of the equipment for the environment.
(ii)   earthing and bonding.
(iii) connection to the supply.
(iv) use of accessories of the correct Degree of Protection (IP code).

8.3 Data processing and other equipment with high leakage current in Small Commercial and Industrial installations

For information on data processing refer to Section 607 of the 16th Edition of the IEE Wiring Regulations.

9. INSPECTION AND TESTING

9.1 Inspection and Testing

Every installation must be inspected and tested during erection and/or on completion before being put into service.

Test methods must be such that no danger to people, livestock or property, or damage to equipment, can occur even if the circuit is defective.

If the inspection and test are satisfactory a completion and inspection certificate (as in Appendix 8) is to be given to the customer.

9.2 Inspection

9.2.1 Detailed inspection must precede testing and must, normally, be done with that part of the installation under inspection disconnected from the supply.

The purpose of the inspection is to verify that equipment is:

(i) correctly selected and erected in accordance with the 16th Edition of the IEE Wiring Regulations.

(ii) not visibly damaged or defective so as to impair safety.

9.2.2 Inspection checklist

The inspection shall include the checking of relevant items from the following checklist:

(i)   connection of conductors.

(ii)   identification of conductors.

(iii)   routing of cable in safe zones or within mechanical protection.

(iv)   selection of conductors for current-carrying capacity and voltage drop, in accordance with the design.

(v)   connection of single-pole devices for protection or switching in phase conductors only.

(vi)   correct connection of socket-outlets and lampholders.

(vii)   presence of fire barriers and protection against thermal effects.

(viii) methods of protection against direct contact, i.e.:
        (a) protection by insulation of live parts.
        (b) protection by barriers or enclosures.

(ix)　methods of protection against indirect contact, i.e.:
　　　(a) presence of circuit protective conductors.
　　　(b) presence of earthing conductors.
　　　(c) presence of main equipotential bonding conductors.
　　　(d) presence of supplementary equipotential bonding
　　　　　conductors.
　　　(e) use of Class II equipment or equivalent insulation.

(x)　prevention of mutual detrimental influence.

Account must be taken of the proximity of other categories
of circuitry and of non-electrical services and influences.

Fire alarm and emergency lighting circuits must be separated
from other cables and from each other, in compliance with
BS 5839 and BS 5266.

Category 1 and category 2 circuit cables may not be present
in the same enclosure or wiring system unless they are either
separated by an effective barrier or wired with cables suited
to the highest voltage present. Where common boxes are
used for category 1 and category 2 circuits, the circuits must
be segregated by an insulating or earthed partition.

Except for category 3 mics cables to BS 6207 or cables
complying with BS 6387 category 3 cables must be separated
completely from other cables by a suitable partition

Mixed categories of circuits may be contained in multicore
cables subject to specific requirements.

Definitions of circuit categories

Category 1 circuit.

A circuit (other than a fire alarm or emergency lighting
circuit) operating at low voltage and supplied directly from a
mains supply system.

Category 2 circuit.

With the exception of fire alarm and emergency lighting
circuits, any circuit for telecommunication (e.g., radio,
telephone, sound distribution, intruder alarm, bell and call,
and data transmission circuit) which is supplied at extra-low
voltage.

Category 3 circuit.

A fire alarm circuit or an emergency lighting circuit.

(xi)　presence of appropriate devices for isolation and
　　　switching.

(xii) presence of undervoltage protective devices (where appropriate).

(xiii) choice and setting of protective and monitoring devices (for protection against indirect contact and/or protection against overcurrent).

(xiv) labelling of circuits, fuses, switches and terminals.

(xv) selection of equipment and protective measures appropriate to external influences.

(xvi) adequacy of access to switchgear and equipment.

(xvii) presence of danger notices and other warning notices.

(xviii) presence of diagrams, instructions and similar information.

(xix) erection methods.

9.3 Testing

Testing shall include the relevant tests from the following checklist.

When a test shows a fault, that fault must be corrected. The test must then be repeated, as must any earlier test that could have been influenced by the fault.

9.3.1 Testing Checklist

(i) continuity of protective conductors (including main and supplementary bonding conductors).

(ii) continuity of ring final circuit conductors.

(iii) insulation resistance (between phase and neutral conductors and between each of these and earth).

(iv) polarity, this includes checks that single-pole control and protective devices (e.g. switches, fuses) are connected in the phase conductor only, that centre-contact bayonet and Edison-screw lamp-holders complying with BS 6776 have their outer contacts connected to the neutral conductor and that wiring has been correctly connected to socket-outlets.

(v) earth fault loop impedance.

(vi) earth electrode resistance.

(vii) operation of r.c.ds.

10. GUIDANCE NOTES ON INITIAL TESTING OF INSTALLATIONS

10.1 Safety

Electrical testing involves hazard. It is the tester's duty to ensure his own safety, and the safety of others, in the performance of his test procedures. When using test instruments, this is best achieved by precautions such as:

(i) understanding the equipment to be used.

(ii) observing safety procedures set out in the Health and Safety Executive Guidance Note GS 38.

(iii) checking that the instruments being used conform to the appropriate British Standard safety specifications. These are BS 4743 for electronic instruments and BS 5458 for electrical instruments.

(iv) checking that test leads including any prods or clips used are in good order, are clean and have no cracked or broken insulation.

The requirements for test leads of the Health & Safety Executive Guidance Note GS 38 'Electrical test equipment for use by electricians' should be observed. This requires the use of fused test leads aimed primarily at reducing the risks associated with arcing under fault conditions.

10.2 Sequence of Tests

Tests should be carried out in the following sequence:

10.2.1 Before the supply is connected

(i)   continuity of protective conductors, main and supplementary bonding.
(ii)   continuity of ring final circuit conductors.
(iii) polarity.
(iv)   insulation resistance.
(v)   earth electrode resistance.

10.2.2 With the supply connected

(vi)   re-check polarity before further testing.
(vii) earth fault loop impedance.
(viii) operation of residual current-operated device.
(ix)   prospective short-circuit current (p.s.c.c.) measurement, if applicable.

Results obtained during various tests should be recorded for future reference.

10.3 Test Procedures

10.3.1 Continuity of protective and bonding conductors (except ring final circuits, see 10.3.2)

Every protective conductor including the earthing conductor, main and supplementary bonding conductors should be tested to verify that the conductors are electrically sound and correctly connected.

The test methods detailed below, as well as checking the continuity of the protective conductor, also provide a measure of $(R_1 + R_2)$. Note: $(R_1 + R_2)$ is considered to be the sum of the resistances of the line conductor(s) (R_1) and the circuit protective conductor(s) (R_2) between the point of utilisation and origin of the installation.

Use an ohmmeter capable of measuring a low resistance for these tests.

10.3.1(i) To test the continuity of protective conductors

Test Method 1

Bridge the phase conductor to the protective conductor at the distribution switchboard so as to include all the circuit. Then test between phase and earth terminals at each outlet in the circuit. The measurement at the circuit's extremity should be recorded and is the value of $(R_1 + R_2)$ for the circuit under test (see Fig.10.1).

This test should be done before connecting supplementary bonds to the protective conductors.

Test Method 2

Connect one terminal of the continuity tester to a long test lead and connect this to the consumer's main earthing terminal.

Connect the other terminal of the continuity tester to another test lead and use this to make contact with the protective conductor at various points on the circuit, such as luminaires, switches, spur outlets etc.

The resistance reading from this test method includes the resistance of the test leads which should be measured and deducted from the resistance readings obtained.

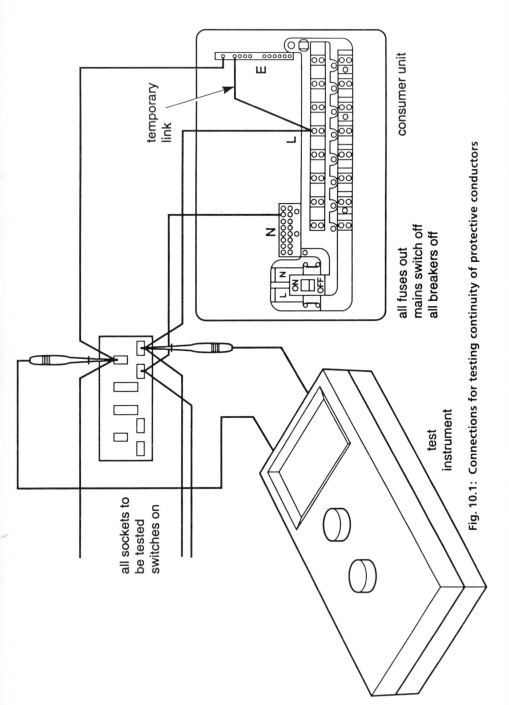

temporary
link

E

L

N

consumer unit

all fuses out
mains switch off
all breakers off

all sockets to
be tested
switches on

test
instrument

Fig. 10.1: Connections for testing continuity of protective conductors

32

10.3.1(ii) To test the continuity of bonding conductors

Use Test Method 2

Note: These Test methods are applicable only to an 'all-insulated' installation.

Installations which use;

(a) armoured cables.

(b) ferrous enclosures (conduit, trunking, steel armouring etc).

as protective conductors are outside the scope of this Guide and a test method is not given. Refer to the Guidance Notes on Inspecting and Testing.

10.3.2 Continuity of ring final circuit conductors

A test is required to verify the continuity of the phase, neutral and protective conductors of every final ring circuit. The test results show if the ring has been inter-connected to create an apparent continuous ring circuit which is in fact broken.

With each leg of the ring circuit identified, the phase conductor of one leg and the neutral conductor of the other leg are temporarily bridged. The resistance is measured between the remaining phase and neutral conductors; a finite reading confirms that there is no open circuit on the ring conductors under test. These remaining conductors are then temporarily bridged (see Fig.10.2).

Where the protective conductor has to be a ring, the test is repeated, transposing the circuit protective conductor with one of the live conductors. The selected live conductor from one leg of the ring is temporarily bridged with the circuit protective conductor of the other leg of the ring. The resistance is measured between the remaining selected live conductor and the remaining unconnected circuit protective conductor at the origin of the circuit. A finite reading confirms that there is no open circuit on the ring conductors under test.

The remaining circuit protective conductor and selected live conductor are then temporarily bridged together.

The resistance is measured between the circuit protective conductor and selected live conductor contacts at each socket outlet around the ring. The readings obtained should be substantially the same, provided that no multiple loops

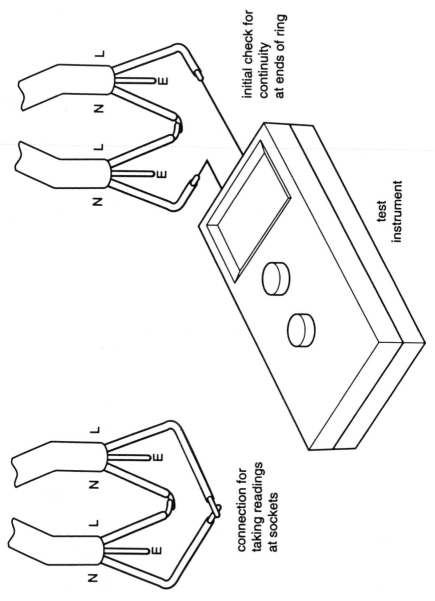

initial check for continuity at ends of ring

test instrument

connection for taking readings at sockets

Fig. 10.2: Connections for testing continuity of ring final circuit conductors

exist, and are equal to $(R_1 + R_2)$ for the circuit. The readings should be recorded.

Note: Where single-core cables are used, special care should be taken to verify that the phase and neutral conductors of opposite ends of the ring circuit are bridged together. An error in this respect will be apparent from the readings taken at the socket-outlets, progressively increasing in value as readings are taken towards the midpoint of the ring, then progressively decreasing towards the other end of the ring.

10.3.3 Polarity

The method of test is the same as for checking the continuity of protective conductors which may have already been carried out (see 10.3.1 and Fig.10.1).

For radial circuits, the R_1 and R_2 measurements made in Test Method 1 should be made at each point, then repeated with the phase and neutral strapped together at the distribution board, and the test made between the switch line and neutral at the light point, or phase to neutral at the equipment (see Fig.10.3).

10.3.4 Insulation resistance

Pre-test checks

10.3.4(i)

(a) pilot or indicator lamps, and capacitors, are disconnected from circuits to avoid an inaccurate test value being obtained.

(b) voltage-sensitive electronic devices such as dimmer switches, touch switches, delay timers, power controllers, electronic starters for fluorescent lamps etc., should be temporarily disconnected so that they are not subjected to the test voltage. It should be confirmed that there are no r.c.ds. incorporating electronic amplifiers.

10.3.4(ii)

Tests should be made using the appropriate d.c. test voltage specified in Table 10.1.

The tests should be made with all fuses in place, switches and circuit breakers closed, lamps removed and other current-using equipment disconnected. Where the removal of lamps and/or the disconnection of current-using equipment is impracticable, the local switches controlling such lamps and/or equipment should be open.

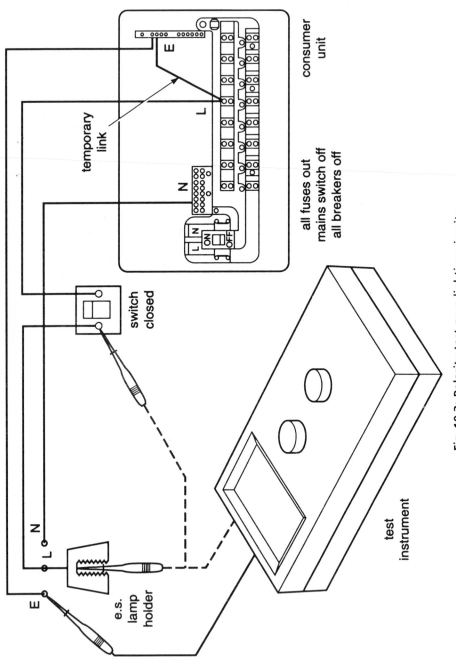

Fig. 10.3: Polarity test on a lighting circuit:

temporary link

consumer unit

all fuses out
mains switch off
all breakers off

switch closed

test instrument

e.s. lamp holder

E N L

TABLE 10.1

Minimum values of insulation resistance

Circuit nominal voltage	Test voltage V d.c.	Minimum insulation resistance (M ohms)	
Extra-low voltage circuits when the circuit is supplied from a safety isolating transformer	250	0.25	✗
Up to and including 500 V with the exception of the above cases	500	0.5	✶

Where electronic devices are disconnected for the purpose of the tests on the installation wiring (and the devices have exposed conductive parts required by the 16th Edition of the IEE Wiring Regulations to be connected to the protective conductors) the insulation resistance between the exposed conductive parts and all live parts of the device shall be measured separately and shall not be less than the values stated in Table 10.1.

10.3.4(iii) Insulation resistance between live conductors

Single-phase

Test between the phase and neutral conductors at the distribution board or consumer unit (see Fig.10.4).

Three-phase

Make a series of tests between live conductors in turn, two by two, at the distribution board as follows:

(1) Between phase 1 and phase 2, phase 3 and the neutral joined.
(2) Between phase 2 and phase 3 and the neutral joined.
(3) Between phase 3 and the neutral.

Where it is more convenient, conductors may be joined together for the purposes of this test. Resistance readings obtained should not be less than the minimum values referred to in Table 10.1.

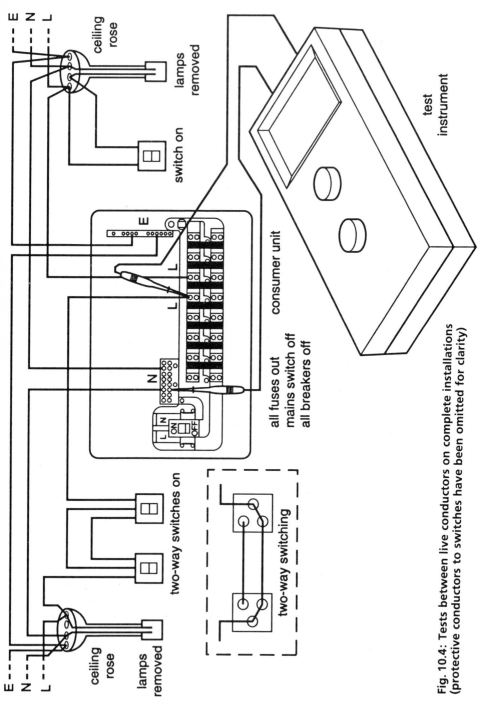

Fig. 10.4: Tests between live conductors on complete installations (protective conductors to switches have been omitted for clarity)

E
N
L

ceiling rose

lamps removed

switch on

consumer unit

E

L L

L

N

all fuses out
mains switch off
all breakers off

ON OFF
L N

test instrument

two-way switches on

two-way switching

ceiling rose

lamps removed

E
N
L

10.3.4(iv) Insulation resistance to Earth (see Fig. 10.5).

Single-phase

Test between the live and the circuit protective conductors at the distribution board or consumer unit.

Three-phase

Make a series of tests between live conductors and protective conductor in turn at the distribution board as follows:

(1) Phase 1 to protective conductor.
(2) Phase 2 to protective conductor.
(3) Phase 3 to protective conductor.
(4) Neutral to protective conductor.

Resistance readings obtained should not be less than the minimum values referred to in Table 10.1.

Where any circuits contain two-way switching the two-way switches must be operated and another insulation resistance test carried out on the strapping wire which was not previously included in the test.

Protection by FELV and Separation of Circuits

This Guide does not cover testing of these items. Such testing is a specialised function requiring instruments not generally available to installers and specialist advice is required.

10.3.5 Earth electrode resistance

If the electrode under test is being used in conjunction with an r.c.d. protecting an installation, the following method of test may be applied.

Before this test is undertaken, any equipotential bonding should be disconnected from the earth electrode to ensure that the test current passes through the earth electrode alone. Remember to reconnect afterwards.

A loop impedance tester is connected between the phase conductor at the source of the installation and the earth electrode, and a test performed. This impedance reading is treated as the electrode resistance and is then added to the resistance of the protective conductor for the protected circuits.

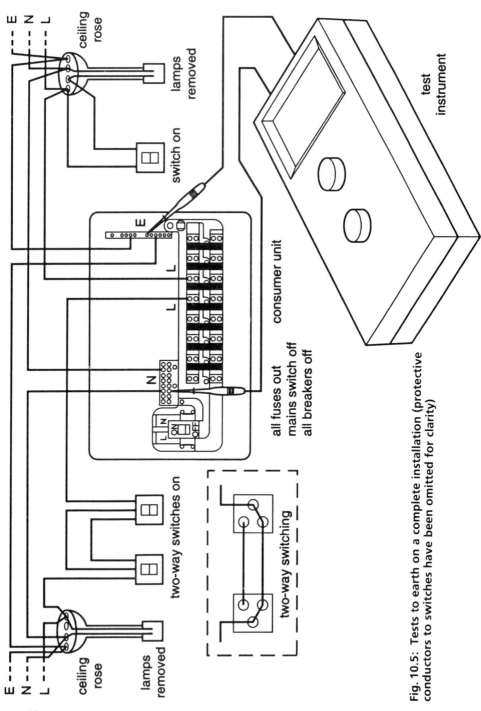

Fig. 10.5: Tests to earth on a complete installation (protective conductors to switches have been omitted for clarity)

40

The results should be at most as Section 4.2 (see 10.3.6). Acceptable test results will depend upon the application of the following:

(i) for TT systems, the value of the earth electrode resistance in ohms multiplied by the operating current in amps of the protective device shall not exceed 50 volts.

(ii) for TN or TT systems, when protection is afforded by an r.c.d., the rated residual operating current in amperes times the earth fault loop impedance in ohms should not exceed 50 volts. This test should be carried out before energising other parts of the system.

The impedance measurement is made between the phase and earth at the origin of the installation. The means of earthing will be isolated from the installation earthed equipotential bonding for the duration of the test. Care should be taken to avoid any shock hazard to the testing personnel and to other persons on the site whilst establishing contact and performing the test.

10.3.6 Earth fault loop impedance

The earth fault loop impedance (Z_s) should be determined at the farthest point of each circuit including socket-outlets, lighting and any other fixed equipment.

The external impedance (Z_e) is measured using a phase-earth loop impedance tester at the origin of the installation (see Fig. 10.6).

The impedance measurement is made between the phase and earth at the origin of the installation. The means of earthing will be isolated from the installation earthed equipotential bonding for the duration of the test. Care should be taken to avoid any shock hazard to the testing personnel and to other persons on the site whilst establishing contact and performing the test.

Note: For further information on the measurement of earth fault loop impedance, refer to the Guidance Notes on Reference Tests for the Initial and Periodic Testing of Electrical Installations.

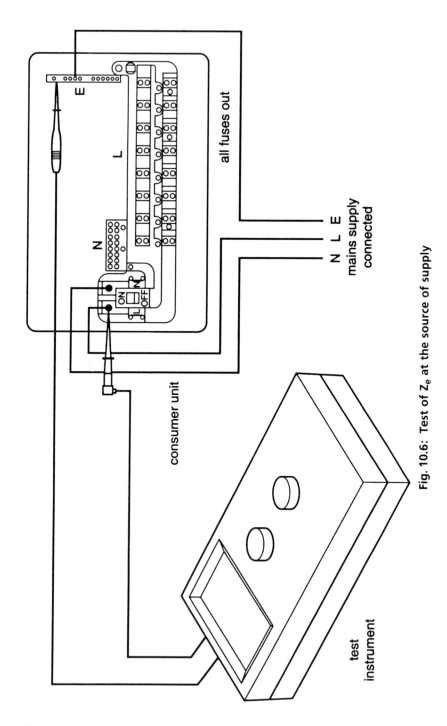

E

L

N

all fuses out

N L E
mains supply
connected

consumer unit

test
instrument

Fig. 10.6: Test of Z_e at the source of supply

11. OPERATION OF RESIDUAL CURRENT OPERATED DEVICES

11.1 General Test Procedure

The tests are made on the load side of the r.c.d., as near as practicable to the point of utilisation, and between the phase conductor of the circuit protected and the associated circuit protective conductor. The load supplied should be disconnected during the test.

11.2 R.C.Ds. to BS 4293

(i)   with a fault current flowing equivalent to 50% of the rated tripping current of the r.c.d. for a period of 2 s, the device should not open.

(ii) with a fault current flowing equivalent to 100% of the rated tripping current of the r.c.d., the device will open in less than 200 ms.

Where the r.c.d. incorporates an intentional time delay it should trip within the time range of 50% of the rated time delay plus 200 ms and 100% of the rated time range plus 200 ms.

Because of the variability of the time delay it is not possible to specify a maximum test time. It is therefore imperative that the circuit protective conductor does not rise more than 50 volts above earth potential - see Regulation 413-02. It is suggested that in practice a 2 s maximum test time is sufficient.

(iii) where the r.c.d. is used to provide supplementary protection against direct contact in accordance with Regulation 412-06-02, with a test current of 150 mA the device should open in less than 40 ms. The maximum test time must not be longer than 50 ms.

11.3 Integral Test Device

An integral test device is incorporated in each r.c.d. This device enables the mechanical parts of the r.c.d. to be checked.

Tripping the r.c.d. by means of the above electrical tests and the integral test device establishes the following:

(i)   that the r.c.d. is operating within the correct sensitivity.

(ii) the integrity of the electrical and mechanical elements of the tripping device.

Operation of the integral test device does not provide a means of checking:
(a) the continuity of the earthing conductor or the associated circuit protective conductors, or
(b) any earth electrode or other means of earthing, or
(c) any other part of the associated installation earthing.

APPENDICES
CONTENTS

APPENDIX 1

MAXIMUM DEMAND AND DIVERSITY

(See Regulation 311-01-01)

This Appendix gives some information on the determination of the maximum demand for an installation and includes the current demand to be assumed for commonly used equipment. It also includes some notes on the application of allowances for diversity.

The information and values given in this Appendix are intended only for guidance because it is impossible to specify the appropriate allowances for diversity for every type of installation and such allowances call for special knowledge and experience. The figures given in Table 1B, therefore, may be increased or decreased as decided by the engineer responsible for the design of the installation concerned. For blocks of residential dwellings, large hotels, industrial and large commercial premises, the allowances are to be assessed by a competent person.

The current demand of a final circuit is determined by summating the current demands of all points of utilisation and equipment in the circuit and, where appropriate, making an allowance for diversity. Typical current demands to be used for this summation are given in Table 1A.

The current demand of a circuit supplying a number of final circuits may be assessed by using the allowances for diversity given in Table 1B which are applied to the total current demand of all the equipment supplied by that circuit and not by summating the current demands of the individual final circuits obtained as outlined above. In Table 1B the allowances are expressed either as percentages of the current demand or, where followed by the letters f.l., as percentages of the rated full load current of the current-using equipment. The current demand for any final circuit which is a conventional circuit arrangement complying with Appendix 5 is the rated current of the overcurrent protective device of that circuit.

An alternative method of assessing the current demand of a circuit supplying a number of final circuits is to summate the diversified current demands of the individual circuits and then apply a further allowance for diversity. In this method the allowances given in Table 1B are not to be used, the values to be chosen being the responsibility of the designer of the installation.

The use of other methods of determining maximum demand is not precluded where specified by a suitably qualified electrical engineer.

After the design currents for all the circuits have been determined, enabling the conductor sizes to be chosen, it is necessary to check that the limitation on voltage drop is met.

TABLE 1A

Current demand to be assumed for points of utilisation and current-using equipment

Point of utilisation or current-using equipment	Current demand to be assumed
Socket-outlets other than 2 A socket-outlets	Rated current
2 A socket-outlets	At least 0.5 A
Lighting outlet*	Current equivalent to the connected load, with a minimum of 100 W per lamp-holder
Electric clock, shaver supply unit (complying with BS 3535), shaver socket-outlet (complying with BS 4573), bell transformer, and current-using equipment of a rating not greater than 5 VA	May be neglected
Household cooking appliance	The first 10 A of the rated current plus 30% of the remainder of the rated current plus 5 A if a socket-outlet is incorporated in the control unit
All other stationary equipment	British Standard rated current, or normal current

*Note: Final circuits for discharge lighting are arranged so as to be capable of carrying the total steady current, viz. that of the lamp(s) and any associated gear and also their harmonic currents. Where more exact information is not available, the demand in volt-amperes is taken as the rated lamp watts multiplied by not less than 1.8. This multiplier is based upon the assumption that the circuit is correct to a power factor of not less than 0.85 lagging, and takes into account control gear losses and harmonic current.

TABLE 1B

Allowances for diversity

Purpose of final circuit fed from conductors or switchgear to which diversity applies	Type of premises		
	Individual household installations, including individual dwellings of a block	Small shops, stores, offices and business premises	Small hotels, boarding houses, guest houses, etc.
1. Lighting	66% of total current demand	90% of total current demand	75% of total current demand
2. Heating and power (but see 3 and 8 below)	100% of total current demand up to 10 amperes + 50% of any current demand in excess of 10 amperes	100% f.l. of largest appliance + 75% f.l. of remaining appliances	100% f.l. of largest appliance + 80% f.l. of second largest appliance + 60% f.l. of remaining appliances
3. Cooking appliances	10 amperes + 30% f.l. of connected cooking appliances in excess of 10 amperes + 5 amperes if socket-outlet incorporated in unit	100% f.l. of largest appliance + 80% f.l. of second largest appliance + 60% f.l. of remaining appliances	100% f.l. of largest appliance + 80% f.l. of second largest appliance + 60% f.l. of remaining appliances
4. Motors(other than lift motors which are subject to special consideration)		100% f.l. of largest motor + 80% f.l. of second largest motor 60% f.l. of remaining motors	100% f.l. of largest motor + 50% f.l. of remaining motors
5. Water-heaters (instantaneous type)*	100% f.l. of largest appliance + 100% f.l. of second largest appliance + 25% f.l. of remaining appliances	100% f.l. of largest appliance + 100% f.l. of second largest appliance + 25% f.l. of remaining appliances	100% f.l. of largest appliance + 100% f.l. of second largest appliance + 25% f.l. of remaining appliances

48

TABLE 1B continued
Allowances for diversity

Purpose of final circuit fed from conductors or switchgear to which diversity applies	Type of premises		
	Individual household installations, including individual dwellings of a block	Small shops, stores, offices and business premises	Small hotels, boarding houses, guest houses, etc.
6. Water-heaters (thermostatically controlled)	no diversity allowable†		
7. Floor warming installations	no diversity allowable†		
8. Thermal storage space heating installations	no diversity allowable†		
9. Standard arrangements of final circuits in accordance with Appendix 5	100% of current demand of largest circuit + 40% of current demand of every other circuit	100% of current demand of largest circuit + 50% of current demand of every other circuit	
10. Socket-outlets other than those included in 9 above and stationary equipment other than those listed above	100% of current demand of largest point of utilisation + 40% of current demand of every other point of utilisation	100% of current demand of largest point of utilisation + 75% of current demand of every other point of utilisation	100% of current demand of largest point of utilisation + 75% of current demand of every point in main rooms (dining rooms, etc) + 40% of current demand of every other point of utilisation

* For the purpose of this Table an instantaneous water-heater is deemed to be a water-heater of any loading which heats water only while the tap is turned on and therefore uses electricity intermittently.

† It is important to ensure that the distribution boards are of sufficient rating to take the total load connected to them without the application of any diversity.

APPENDIX 2

LIMITATION OF EARTH FAULT LOOP IMPEDANCE FOR COMPLIANCE WITH REGULATION 543-01-01

Regulation 543-01 indicates that the cross-sectional area of a protective conductor, other than an equipotential bonding conductor, shall be:

(i) calculated in accordance with Regulation 543-01-03
(ii) determined in accordance with Regulation 543-01-04

In some cases the type of cable it is intended to use determines which of the two methods can be followed. For instance, the widely used flat twin and flat three-core p.v.c.-insulated and p.v.c.-sheathed cables with protective conductors (cables to Table 5 of BS 6004) do not comply with Table 54G of Regulation 543-01-04 (other than the 1 mm^2 size) and therefore method (i) must be used.

Where method (i) is used, in order to apply the formula given in Regulation 543-01-03 it is essential that the time/current characteristic of the overcurrent protective device in the circuit concerned is available. A selection of such characteristics for fuses and miniature circuit breakers is given in Appendix 3 of the 16th Edition. For other types of these devices the advice of the manufacturer has to be sought. The time/current characteristics given in Appendix 3 indicate the maximum disconnection times for the devices concerned and give coordinates for fixed times.

Assuming that the size and type of cable to be used have already been determined from consideration of other aspects such as the magnitude of the design current of the circuit and the limitation of voltage drop under normal load conditions, the first stage is to calculate the earth fault loop impedance, Z_s. If the cable it is intended to use does not incorporate a protective conductor, that conductor has to be chosen separately.

For cables having conductors of cross-sectional area not exceeding 35 mm^2, their inductance can be ignored so that where these cables are used in radial circuits, the earth fault loop impedance Z_s is given by:

$$Z_s = Z_e + R_1 + R_2 \text{ ohms}$$

Where Z_e is that part of the earth fault loop impedance external to the circuit concerned, R_1 is the resistance of the phase conductor from the origin of the circuit to the most distant socket-outlet or other point of utilisation, and R_2 is the resistance of the protective conductor from the origin of the circuit to the most distant socket-outlet or other point of utilisation.

Similarly, where such cables are used in a ring circuit without spurs, the earth fault loop impedance Z_s is given by:

$$Z_s = Z_e + 0.25\,R_1 + 0.25\,R_2 \text{ ohms}$$

Where Z_e is as described above, R_1 is now the total resistance of the phase conductor between its ends prior to them being connected together to complete the ring, and R_2 is similarly the total resistance of the protective conductor.

Note: Strictly the above equations are vectorial but arithmetic addition to determine the earth fault loop impedance may be used, as it gives a pessimistically high value for that impedance.

Having determined Z_s, the earth fault current I_f, is given by:

$$I_f = \frac{U_o}{Z_s} \text{ amperes}$$

where U_o is the nominal voltage to earth (phase to neutral voltage).

From the relevant time/current characteristic the time for disconnection (t) corresponding to this earth fault current is obtained.

Substitution for I_f, t and the appropriate k value in the equation given in Regulation 543-01-03 then gives the minimum cross-sectional area of protective conductor and this has to be equal to or less than the size chosen.

When the cables to be used are to Table 5 of BS 6004, or are other p.v.c.-insulated cables to the relevant BS, then Tables 2A and 2C give the maximum earth loop impedance for circuits with;

(a) protective conductors of copper and having from 1 mm² to 16 mm² cross-sectional area,

(b) where the overcurrent protective device is a fuse in BS 88 Part 2 and Part 6, BS 1361 or BS 3036.

The tables also apply if the protective conductor is bare copper and in contact with cable insulated with p.v.c.

For each type of fuse, two tables are given:

— where the circuit concerned feeds socket-outlets and the disconnection time for compliance with Regulation 413-02 is 0.4 s, and

— where the circuit concerned feeds fixed equipment and the disconnection time for compliance with Regulation 413-02 is 5 s.

In each table the earth fault loop impedances given correspond to the appropriate disconnection time from a comparison of the time/current characteristic of the device concerned and the equation given in Regulation 543-01-03.

The tabulated values apply only when the nominal voltage to Earth (U_o) is 240 Volts.

For circuits protected by m.c.bs. compliance with Table 41B2 affords compliance with Regulation 543-01-01 where the protective conductors range from 1 mm^2 to 16 mm^2 cross-sectional area and the rated current of the m.c.bs. ranges from 5 A to 50 A.

For guidance on conductor resistances, see Appendix 6.

TABLE 2A

Maximum earth fault loop impedance (in ohms) when overcurrent protective device is a fuse to BS 3036

(i) For circuits feeding socket-outlets

Protective conductor mm^2	Fuse rating, amperes				
	5	15	20	30	45
1	10	2.67	1.85	—	—
1.5	10	2.67	1.85	1.14	—
2.5	10	2.67	1.85	1.14	0.62
4	10	2.67	1.85	1.14	0.62
6	10	2.67	1.85	1.14	0.62
10	10	2.67	1.85	1.14	0.62
16	10	2.67	1.85	1.14	0.62

(ii) For circuits feeding fixed equipment

Protective conductor mm^2	Fuse rating, amperes				
	5	15	20	30	45
1	18.5	5.58	—	—	—
1.5	18.5	5.58	4.0	—	—
2.5	18.5	5.58	4.0	2.76	—
4	18.5	5.58	4.0	2.76	1.66
6	18.5	5.58	4.0	2.76	1.66
10	18.5	5.58	4.0	2.76	1.66
16	18.5	5.58	4.0	2.76	1.66

TABLE 2B

Maximum earth fault loop impedance (in ohms) when overcurrent protective device is a fuse to BS 88 Part 2 or Part 6

(i) For circuits feeding socket-outlets

Protective conductor mm²	Fuse rating, amperes							
	6	10	16	20	25	32	40	50
1	8.89	5.33	2.82	1.85	1.50	—	—	—
1.5	8.89	5.33	2.82	1.85	1.50	1.09	—	—
2.5	8.89	5.33	2.82	1.85	1.50	1.09	0.86	0.63
4	8.89	5.33	2.82	1.85	1.50	1.09	0.86	0.63
6	8.89	5.33	2.82	1.85	1.50	1.09	0.86	0.63
10	8.89	5.33	2.82	1.85	1.50	1.09	0.86	0.63
16	8.89	5.33	2.82	1.85	1.50	1.09	0.86	0.63

(ii) For circuits feeding fixed equipment

Protective conductor mm²	Fuse rating, amperes							
	6	10	16	20	25	32	40	50
1	14.1	7.74	—	—	—	—	—	—
1.5	14.1	7.74	4.36	—	—	—	—	—
2.5	14.1	7.74	4.36	3.04	2.40	1.92	—	—
4	14.1	7.74	4.36	3.04	2.40	1.92	1.41	—
6	14.1	7.74	4.36	3.04	2.40	1.92	1.41	1.09
10	14.1	7.74	4.36	3.04	2.40	1.92	1.41	1.09
16	14.1	7.74	4.36	3.04	2.40	1.92	1.41	1.09

TABLE 2C

Maximum earth fault loop impedance (in ohms) when overcurrent protective device is a fuse to BS 1361

(i) For circuits feeding socket-outlets

Protective conductor mm²	Fuse rating, amperes				
	5	15	20	30	45
1	10.9	3.43	1.78	—	—
1.5	10.9	3.43	1.78	1.20	—
2.5	10.9	3.43	1.78	1.20	0.60
4	10.9	3.43	1.78	1.20	0.60
6	10.9	3.43	1.78	1.20	0.60
10	10.9	3.43	1.78	1.20	0.60
16	10.9	3.43	1.78	1.20	0.60

(ii) For circuits feeding fixed equipment

Protective conductor mm²	Fuse rating, amperes				
	5	15	20	30	45
1	17.1	5.22	—	—	—
1.5	17.1	5.22	—	—	—
2.5	17.1	5.22	2.93	1.92	—
4	17.1	5.22	2.93	1.92	—
6	17.1	5.22	2.93	1.92	1.00
10	17.1	5.22	2.93	1.92	1.00
16	17.1	5.22	2.93	1.92	1.00

APPENDIX 3

NOTES ON THE SELECTION OF TYPES OF CABLE AND FLEXIBLE CORD FOR PARTICULAR USES AND EXTERNAL INFLUENCES

For compliance with the requirements of Chapter 52 for the selection and erection of wiring systems in relation to risks of mechanical damage and corrosion, this Appendix lists in two tables types of cable and flexible cord suitable for the uses intended. These tables are not intended to be exhaustive and other limitations may be imposed by the relevant Regulation of the 16th Edition of the IEE Wiring Regulations, in particular those concerning maximum permissible operating temperatures.

Information is also included in this Appendix on protection against corrosion of exposed metalwork of wiring systems.

TABLE 3A

Applications of cables for fixed wiring

Type of cable	Uses	Additional precautions (if any)
P.V.C.-or rubber-insulated non-sheathed	In conduits, cable ducting or trunking, but not in such conduits etc. buried underground	
Light circular p.v.c.-insulated and sheathed	(i) General indoor use other than embedding (ii) Underground in conduit or pipes	Additional protection where exposed to severe mechanical stresses
Flat p.v.c.-insulated and sheathed	(i) General indoor use (ii) On exterior surface walls, boundary walls and the like (iii) Overhead wiring between buildings (iv) Underground in conduits or pipes	Additional protection where exposed to severe mechanical stresses

TABLE 3A continued

Applications of cables for fixed wiring

Type of cable	Uses	Additional precautions (if any)
Split-concentric p.v.c.-insulated	General	
Consac	General	
Mineral-insulated	General	With overall p.v.c. covering where exposed to the weather or risk of corrosion, or where installed underground, or in concrete ducts
P.V.C.-insulated and armoured	General	With overall p.v.c. covering where exposed to the weather or risk of corrosion, or where installed underground, or in concrete ducts
Paper-insulated lead-sheathed	General	(i) With armouring where exposed to severe mechanical stresses or where installed underground (ii) With serving where installed in concrete ducts

Notes:

1—The use of cable covers (preferably conforming to BS 2484) or equivalent mechanical protection is desirable for all underground cables which might otherwise subsequently be disturbed.

2—Cables having p.v.c. insulation or sheath should preferably not be used where the ambient temperature is consistently below 0°C. Where they are to be installed during a period of low temperature, precautions should be taken to avoid risk of mechanical damage during handling.

TABLE 3B

Applications of flexible cords

Type of flexible cord	Uses
60°C rubber-insulated braided twin and three-core	Indoors in household or commercial premises where subject only to low mechanical stresses
60°C rubber-insulated and sheathed	(i) Indoors in household or commercial premises where subject only to low mechanical stresses (ii) Occasional use outdoors
60°C rubber-insulated sheathed and screened	Portable hand-held lamps on construction sites or similar applications
60°C rubber-insulated oil-resisting and flame retardant sheath	(i) General, unless subject to severe mechanical stresses (ii) Fixed installations protected in conduit or other enclosure
85°C rubber-insulated HOFR sheathed	General, including hot situations e.g. night storage heaters and immersion heaters
185°C heat resisting p.v.c.-insulated and sheathed (to BS 6500 (1969))	General, including hot situations e.g. for pendant luminaires
150°C rubber-insulated and braided	(i) At high ambient temperatures (ii) In or on luminaires
185°C glass-fibre-insulated single-core twisted twin and three-core	For internal wiring of luminaires only and then only where permitted by BS 4533

Applications of flexible cords

Type of flexible cord	Uses
185°C glass-fibre-insulated braided circular	(i) Dry situations at high ambient temperatures and not subject to abrasions or undue flexing (ii) Wiring of luminaires
Light p.v.c.-insulated and sheathed	Indoors in household or commercial premises in dry situations, for light duty
Ordinary p.v.c.-insulated and sheathed	(i) Indoors in household or commercial premises, including damp situations, for medium duty (ii) For cooking and heating appliances where not in contact with hot parts (iii) For outdoor use other than in agricultural or industrial applications

Protection against corrosion of exposed metalwork or wiring systems

In damp situations, where metal cable sheaths and armour of cables, metal conduit and conduit fittings, metal ducting and trunking systems, and associated metal fixings, are liable to chemical or electrolytic attack by materials of a structure with which they may come in contact, it is necessary to take suitable precautions against corrosion.

Materials likely to cause such attack include:

— materials containing magnesium chloride which are used in the construction of floors and dadoes,

— plaster undercoats contaminated with corrosive salts,

— lime, cement and plaster, for example on unpainted walls,

— oak and other acidic woods,

— dissimilar metals liable to set up electrolytic action.

Application of suitable coatings before erection, or prevention of contact by separation with plastics, are recognized as effectual precautions against corrosion.

Special care is required in the choice of materials for clips and other fittings for bare aluminium-sheathed cables and for aluminium conduit, to avoid risk of local corrosion in damp situations. Examples of suitable materials for this purpose are the following:

— porcelain,

— plastics,

— aluminium,

— corrosion-resistant aluminium alloys,

— zinc alloys complying with BS 1004,

— iron or steel protected against corrosion by galvanizing, sherardizing, etc.

Contact between bare aluminium sheaths or aluminium conduits and any parts made of brass or other metal having a high copper content, should be especially avoided in damp situations, unless the parts are suitably plated. If such contact is unavoidable, the joint should be completely protected against ingress of moisture. Wiped joints in aluminium-sheathed cables should always be protected against moisture by a suitable paint, by an impervious tape, or by embedding in bitumen.

NOTES

APPENDIX 4

NOTES ON METHODS OF SUPPORT FOR CABLES, CONDUCTORS AND WIRING SYSTEMS

This Appendix describes examples of methods of support for cables, conductors and wiring systems which satisfy the relevant requirements of Chapter 52 of the Regulations. The use of other methods is not precluded where specified by a suitably qualified electrical engineer.

Cables generally

Items 1 to 8 below are generally applicable to supports on structures which are subject only to vibration of low severity and a low risk of mechanical impact.

1. For non-sheathed cables, installation in conduit without further fixing of the cables, precautions being taken against undue compression or other mechanical stressing of the insulation at the top of any vertical runs exceeding 5 m in length.

2. For cables of any type, installation in ducting or trunking without further fixing of the cables, vertical runs not exceeding 5 m in length without intermediate support.

3. For sheathed and/or armoured cables installed in accessible positions, support by clips at spacings not exceeding the appropriate value stated in Table 4A.

4. For cables of any type, resting without fixing in horizontal runs of ducts, conduits, cable ducting or trunking.

5. For sheathed and/or armoured cables in horizontal runs which are inaccessible and unlikely to be disturbed, resting without fixing on part of a building, the surface of that part being reasonably smooth.

6. For sheathed-and-armoured cables in vertical runs which are inaccessible and unlikely to be disturbed, supported at the top of the run by a clip and a rounded support of a radius not less than the appropriate value stated in Table 4E.

7. For sheathed cables without armour in vertical runs which are inaccessible and unlikely to be disturbed, supported by the method described in Item 6 above; the length of run without intermediate support not

exceeding 2 m for a lead-sheathed cable or 5 m for a rubber or p.v.c.-sheathed cable.

8. For rubber or p.v.c.-sheathed cables, installation in conduit without further fixing of the cables, any vertical runs being in conduit of suitable size and not exceeding 5 m in length.

Cables in particular conditions

9. In caravans, for sheathed cables in inaccessible spaces such as ceiling, wall, and floor spaces, support at intervals not exceeding 0.25 m for horizontal runs and 0.4 m for vertical runs.

10. In caravans for horizontal runs of sheathed cables passing through floor or ceiling joists in inaccessible floor or ceiling spaces, securely bedded in thermal insulating material, no further fixing is required.

11. For flexible cords used as pendants, attachment to a ceiling rose or similar accessory by the cord grip or other method of strain relief provided in the accessory.

12. For temporary installations and installations on construction sites, supports so arranged that there is no appreciable mechanical strain on any cable termination or joint.

Overhead wiring

13. For cables sheathed with rubber or p.v.c., supported by a separate catenary wire, either continuously bound up with the cable or attached thereto at intervals; the intervals not exceeding those stated in Column 2 of Table 4A.

14. Support by a catenary wire incorporated in the cable during manufacture, the spacings between supports not exceeding those stated by the manufacturer and the minimum height above ground being in accordance with Table 4B.

15. For spans without intermediate support (e.g. between buildings) of p.v.c.-insulated p.v.c.-sheathed cable, or rubber-insulated cable having an oil-resisting and flame retardant or h.o.f.r. sheath, terminal supports so arranged that no undue strain is placed upon the conductors or insulation of the cable, adequate precautions being taken against any risk of chafing of the cable sheath, and the minimum height above

ground and the length of such spans being in accordance with the appropriate values indicated in Table 4B.

16. Bare or p.v.c.-covered conductors of an overhead line for distribution between a building and a remote point of utilisation (e.g. another building) supported on insulators, the lengths of span and heights above ground having the appropriate values indicated in Table 4B or otherwise installed in accordance with the Electricity Supply Regulations 1988 (as amended).

17. For spans without intermediate support (e.g. between buildings) and which are in situations inaccessible to vehicular traffic, cables installed in heavy gauge steel conduit, the length of span and height above ground being in accordance with Table 4B.

Conduit and cable trunking

18. Rigid conduit supported in accordance with Table 4C.

19. Cable trunking supported in accordance with Table 4D.

20. Conduit embedded in the material of the building.

21. Pliable conduit embedded in the material of the building or in the ground, or supported in accordance with Table 4C.

TABLE 4A

Spacing of supports for cables in accessible positions

Overall diameter of cable*	Maximum spacing of clips							
	Non-armoured rubber, p.v.c., or lead-sheathed cables				Armoured cables		Mineral-insulated copper-sheathed or aluminium-sheathed cables	
	Generally		In caravans					
	Horizontal†	Vertical†	Horizontal†	Vertical†	Horizontal†	Vertical†	Horizontal†	Vertical†
1	2	3	4	5	6	7	8	9
mm	mm	mm	mm	mm	mm	mm	mm	mm
Not exceeding 9	250	400	250 (for all sizes)	400 (for all sizes)	—	—	600	800
Exceeding 9 and not exceeding 15	300	400			350	450	900	1200
Exceeding 15 and not exceeding 20	350	450			400	550	1500	2000
Exceeding 20 and not exceeding 40	400	550			450	600	—	—

Note: For the spacing of supports for cables of overall diameter exceeding 40 mm, and for single-core cables having conductors of cross-sectional area 300 mm² and larger, the manufacturer's recommendations should be observed.

* For flat cables taken as the dimension of the major axis.

† The spacings stated for horizontal runs may be applied also to runs at an angle of more than 30° from the vertical. For runs at an angle of 30° or less from the vertical, the vertical spacings are applicable.

TABLE 4B

Maximum lengths of span and minimum heights above ground for overhead wiring between buildings etc.

Type of system 1	Maximum length of span 2	At road crossings 3	In positions accessible to vehicular traffic, other than crossings 4	In positions inaccessible to vehicular traffic* 5
	m	m	m	m
Cables sheathed with p.v.c. or having an oil-resisting and flame retardant or h.o.f.r. sheath, without intermediate support (Item 15)	3			3.5
Cables sheathed with p.v.c. or having an oil-resisting and flame retardant or h.o.f.r. sheath, in heavy-gauge steel conduit of diameter not less than 20 mm and not jointed in its span (Item 17)	3	(5.8 for all types)	(5.2 for all types)	3
Bare or p.v.c.-covered overhead lines on insulators without intermediate support (Item 16)	30			3.5
Cables sheathed with p.v.c. or having an oil-resisting and flame retardant or h.o.f.r. sheath, supported by a catenary wire (Item 13)	No limit			3.5
Aerial cable incorporating a catenary wire (Item 14)	Subject to Item 14			3.5

TABLE 4B continued

Maximum lengths of span and minimum heights above ground for overhead wiring between buildings etc.

Type of system 1	Maximum length of span 2	Minimum height of span above ground		
		At road crossings 3	In positions accessible to vehicular traffic, other than crossings 4	In positions inaccess-ible to vehicular traffic* 5
Bare or p.v.c.-covered overhead lines installed in accordance with the Overhead Line Regulations (Item 16)	No limit	(5.8 for all types)	(5.2 for all types)	5.2

* This column is not applicable in agricultural premises

Note: In some special cases, such as in yacht marinas or where large cranes are present, it will be necessary to increase the minimum height of span above ground given in Table 4B.

$$VD = \frac{Mu \times A \times M}{1000} \cdot \frac{8.0 \times 45 \times 10}{1000}$$

TABLE 4C

Spacing of supports for conduits

Nominal size of conduit 1	Maximum distance between supports					
	Rigid Metal		Rigid Insulating		Pliable	
	Horizontal 2	Vertical 3	Horizontal 4	Vertical 5	Horizontal 6	Vertical 7
mm	m	m	m	m	m	m
Not exceeding 16	0.75	1.0	0.75	1.0	0.3	0.5
Exceeding 16 and not exceeding 25	1.75	2.0	1.5	1.75	0.4	0.6
Exceeding 25 and not exceeding 40	2.0	2.25	1.75	2.0	0.6	0.8
Exceeding 40	2.25	2.5	2.0	2.0	0.8	1.0

Note: A flexible conduit is not normally required to be supported in its run.

TABLE 4D

Spacing of supports for cable trunking

Cross-sectional area of trunking	Maximum distance between supports			
	Metal		Insulating	
	Horizontal	Vertical	Horizontal	Vertical
1	2	3	4	5
mm²	m	m	m	m
Exceeding 300 and not exceeding 700	0.75	1.0	0.5	0.5
Exceeding 700 and not exceeding 1500	1.25	1.5	0.5	0.5
Exceeding 1500 and not exceeding 2500	1.75	2.0	1.25	1.25
Exceeding 2500 and not exceeding 5000	3.0	3.0	1.5	2.0
Exceeding 5000	3.0	3.0	1.75	2.0

Notes to Tables 4C and 4D:

1—The spacings tabulated allow for maximum fill of cables permitted by these Regulations and the thermal limits specified in the relevant British Standards. They assume that the conduit or trunking is not exposed to other mechanical stress.

2—The above figures do not apply to lighting suspension trunking, or where special strengthening couplers are used. A flexible conduit is not normally required to be supported in its run. Supports should be positioned within 300 mm of bends or fittings.

TABLE 4E

Minimum internal radii of bends in cables for fixed wiring

Insulation	Finish	Overall diameter*	Factor to be applied to overall diameter of cable to determine minimum internal radius of bend
XLPE, p.v.c or rubber (circular, or circular stranded copper or aluminium conductors)	Non-armoured	Not exceeding 10 mm	3(2)†
		Exceeding 10 mm but not exceeding 25 mm	4(3)†
		Exceeding 25 mm	6
	Armoured	Any	6
XLPE, p.v.c or rubber (solid aluminium or shaped copper conductors)	Armoured non-armoured	Any	8
Mineral	Copper sheath with or without covering	Any	6‡

* For flat cables the diameter refers to the major axis.
† The figure in brackets relates to single-core circular conductors of stranded construction installed in conduit, ducting or trunking.
‡ Mineral-insulated cables may be bent to a radius not less than 3 times the cable diameter over the copper sheath, provided that the bend is not re-worked, i.e. straightened and re-bent.

NOTES

APPENDIX 5

CABLE CAPACITIES OF CONDUIT AND TRUNKING

A number of variable factors affect any attempt to arrive at a standard method of assessing the capacity of conduit or trunking.

Some of these are:

— reasonable care (of drawing-in).

— acceptable use of the space available.

— tolerance in cable sizes.

— tolerance in conduit and trunking.

The following tables can only give guidance of the maximum number of cables which should be drawn in. The sizes should ensure an easy pull with low risk of damage to the cables.

Only the ease of drawing-in is taken into account. The electrical effects of grouping is not. As the number of circuits increases the current-carrying capacity of the cable decreases. Cable sizes have to be increased with consequent increase in cost of cable and conduit.

It may therefore be more attractive economically to divide the circuits concerned between two or more enclosures.

The following three cases are dealt with:

Single-core p.v.c.-insulated cables

(i) in straight runs of conduit not exceeding 3 m in length. Tables 5A & 5B.

(ii) in straight runs of conduit exceeding 3 m in length, or in runs of any length incorporating bends or sets. Tables 5C & 5D.

(iii) in trunking. Tables 5E, 5F & 5G.

Other sizes and types of cable in trunking are dealt with in Table 5G. Convertible terms have been devised to enable the space in the system to be matched to an equivalent group of cables.

For cables and/or conduits, not covered by this Appendix advice on the number of cables which can be drawn in should be obtained from the manufacturers.

Single-core p.v.c.-insulated cables in straight runs of conduit not exceeding 3 m in length.

For each cable it is intended to use, obtain the term from Table 5A.

Add the cable terms together and compare the total with the conduit terms given in Table 5B.

The minimum conduit size is that having a term equal to or greater than the sum of the cable terms.

TABLE 5A

Cable terms
for use in conduit in
short straight runs

TABLE 5B

Conduit terms
for use in
short straight runs

Type of conductor	Conductor cross-sectional area mm^2	Term
Solid	1	22
	1.5	27
	2.5	39
Stranded	1.5	31
	2.5	43
	4	58
	6	88
	10	146
	16	202
	25	385

Conduit diameter mm	Term
16	290
20	460
25	800
32	1400
38	1900
50	3500
63	5600

Single-core p.v.c.-insulated cables in straight runs of conduit exceeding 3 m in length or in runs of any length incorporating bends or sets.

For each cable it is intended to use, obtain the appropriate term from Table 5C.

Add the cable terms together and compare the total with the conduit terms given in Table 5D, taking into account the length of run it is intended to use and the number of bends and sets in that run.

The minimum conduit size is that size having a term equal to or greater than the sum of the cable terms. For the larger sizes of conduit multiplication factors are given relating them to 32 mm diameter conduit.

TABLE 5C

Cable terms for use in conduit in long straight runs over 3 m, or runs of any length incorporating bends

Type of conductor	Conductor cross-sectional area mm²	Term
Solid	1	16
or	1.5	22
stranded	2.5	30
	4	43
	6	58
	10	105
	16	145
	25	217

TABLE 5D

Conduit terms for runs incorporating bends and long straight runs.

Conduit diameter, mm

Length of run m	Straight 16	20	25	32	One bend 16	20	25	32	Two bends 16	20	25	32	Three bends 16	20	25	32	Four bends 16	20	25	32
1	Covered by Tables A and B				188	303	543	947	177	286	514	900	158	256	463	818	130	213	388	692
1.5					182	294	528	923	167	270	487	857	143	233	422	750	111	182	333	600
2					177	286	514	900	158	256	463	818	130	213	388	692	97	159	292	529
2.5					171	278	500	878	150	244	442	783	120	196	358	643	86	141	260	474
3					167	270	487	857	143	233	422	750	111	182	333	600				
3.5	179	290	521	911	162	263	475	837	136	222	404	720	103	169	311	563				
4	177	286	514	900	158	256	463	818	130	213	388	692	97	159	292	529				
4.5	174	282	507	889	154	250	452	800	125	204	373	667	91	149	275	500				
5	171	278	500	878	150	244	442	783	120	196	358	643	86	141	260	474				
6	167	270	487	857	143	233	422	750	111	182	333	600								
7	162	263	475	837	136	222	404	720	103	169	311	563								
8	158	256	463	818	130	213	388	692	97	159	292	529								
9	154	250	452	800	125	204	373	667	91	149	275	500								
10	150	244	442	783	120	196	358	643	86	141	260	474								

Additional Factors: For 38 mm diameter use .... 1.4 x (32 mm term)
For 50 mm diameter use .... 2.6 x (32 mm term)
For 63 mm diameter use .... 4.2 x (32 mm term)

TABLE 5E

Cable terms for trunking

Type of conductor	Conductor cross-sectional area mm²	BESA (DIA)	C.S.A. Term	BESA Term
	(i)	(ii)	(iii)	(iv)
Solid	1.5	3.0	7.1	8.6
	2.5	3.6	10.2	11.9
Stranded	1.5	3.2	8.1	9.6
	2.5	3.8	11.4	13.9
	4	4.4	15.2	18.1
	6	5.4	22.9	22.9
	10	6.8	36.3	36.3
	16	8.0		50.3
	25			75.4
	35			95.0
	50			132.7
	70			176.7
	95			227.0
	120			284.0
	150			346.0
	240			552.0

Note:

(i) These terms are for metal trunking and may be optimistic for plastic trunking where the cross-sectional area available may be significantly reduced from the nominal by the thickness of the wall material.

(ii) The columns (ii) and (iv) headed BESA are those used by the British Electrical Systems Association (BESA) and are based upon diameter, they should be used together with Table 5G.

Columns (i) and (iii) headed cross-sectional area (C.S.A) should be used with Table 5F.

(iii) The provision of spare space is advisable, however, any circuits added at a later date must take into account grouping. Appendix 4, 16th Edition.

Single-core p.v.c.-insulated cables in trunking

For each cable it is intended to use, obtain the appropriate term from Table 5E.

Add all the cable terms so obtained and compare with the terms for trunking given in Table 5F.

The minimum size of trunking is that size having a term equal to or greater than the sum of the cable terms.

TABLE 5F

Terms for trunking

Dimensions of × trunking mm × mm	Term
50 × 37.5	767
50 × 50	1037
75 × 25	738
75 × 37.5	1146
75 × 50	1555
75 × 75	2371
100 × 25	993
100 × 37.5	1542
100 × 50	2091
100 × 75	3189
100 × 100	4252

Space factor—45% with trunking thickness taken into account

BESA TABLE 5G

Terms for trunking

Dimensions of trunking mm × mm		Term
Size	Gauge	
50 × 38	1.0	767
50 × 50	1.0	1037
75 × 25	1.2	738
75 × 38	1.2	1146
75 × 50	1.2	1555
75 × 75	1.2	2371
100 × 25	1.2	993
100 × 38	1.2	1542
100 × 50	1.2	2091
100 × 75	1.2	3189
100 × 100	1.4	4252
150 × 38	1.6	2999
150 × 50	1.6	3091
150 × 75	1.2	4743
150 × 100	1.2	6394
150 × 150	1.6	9697
200 × 38	1.6	3082
200 × 50	1.6	4145
200 × 75	1.6	6359
200 × 100	1.6	8572
200 × 150	1.6	13001
200 × 200	1.6	17429
225 × 38	1.6	3474
225 × 50	1.6	4671
225 × 75	1.6	7167
225 × 100	1.6	9662
225 × 150	1.6	14652
225 × 200	1.6	19643
225 × 225	1.6	22138
300 × 38	1.6	4648
300 × 50	1.6	6251
300 × 75	1.6	9590
300 × 100	1.6	12929
300 × 150	1.6	19607
300 × 200	1.6	26285
300 × 225	1.6	29624
300 × 300	2.0	39428

For other sizes and types of cable or trunking

For sizes and types of cable trunking other than those given in Tables 5E and 5F and BESA 5G above, the number of cables installed should be such that the resulting space factor does not exceed 45% of the net internal cross-sectional area.

Space factor is defined as the ratio (expressed as a percentage) of the sum of the overall cross-sectional areas of cables (insulation and any sheath) to the internal cross-sectional area of the conduit or other cable enclosure in which they are installed. The effective overall cross-sectional area of a non-circular cable is taken as that of a circle of diameter equal to the major axis of the cable.

The minimum internal radii of bends of cables for fixed wiring as given in Table 4E should be used.

APPENDIX 6

RESISTANCE OF COPPER AND ALUMINIUM CONDUCTORS UNDER FAULT CONDITIONS

To check compliance with Regulation 434-03-03 and/or Regulation 543-01-03 i.e. to evaluate the equation $s^2 = I^2t/k^2$ it is necessary to establish the impedances of the circuit conductors to determine the fault current I and hence the protective device disconnection time t.

Similarly, in order to design circuits for compliance with the Regulations the limiting values of earth fault loop impedance given in Tables 41B1 and 41B2 and Appendix 3 of the 16th Edition of the IEE Wiring Regulations or for compliance with the limiting values of the circuit protective conductor Table 41C, it is necessary to establish the relevant impedances of the circuit conductors concerned.

The equation given in Regulations 434-03-03 and 543-01-03 has been based on the assumption of a constant value of fault current, but in practice that current changes during the period of the fault because, due to the rise in temperature, the conductor resistance increases.

The rigorous method for taking into account the changing character of the fault current is too complicated for practical use. Over the range of temperatures encountered in the Regulations a sufficiently accurate method is to calculate conductor impedances on the average of the assumed initial temperature and the maximum permitted final temperature.

For example, for p.v.c-insulated cables the assumed initial temperature is 70°C and the maximum permitted final temperature is 160°C (See Table 54C). The design calculation should therefore be based on (70 + 160)°C ÷ 2 i.e. 115°C and this average value should be used even when the circuit protective conductor and its associated phase conductor are not of the same size.

The following tables are limited to conductor cross-sectional areas up to and including 35 mm², i.e. to conductors having negligible inductance. For larger cables the inductance is not negligible but is independent of temperature and it is necessary to obtain information from the manufacturer as regards the resistive and reactive components of the impedance of the cables it is intended to use.

Table 6A gives values of $(R_1 + R_2)$ per metre for various combinations of conductors of up to and including 35mm² cross-sectional area. (See Appendix 2 for descriptions of R_1 and R_2). It also gives values of resistance per metre for each size of conductor. These values are at 20°C.

Table 6B gives the multipliers to be applied to the values given in Table 6A for the purpose of calculating the resistance under fault conditions of the phase conductors and/or circuit protective conductors in order to determine compliance with, as applicable:

(a) earth fault loop impedance of Table 41B1 or Table 41B2 of the 16th Edition of the IEE Wiring Regulations

(b) equation in Regulation 434-03-03

(c) equation in Regulation 543-01-03

(d) earth fault loop impedance and resistance or protective conductor of Table 41C of the 16th Edition of the IEE Wiring Regulations

(e) earth fault loop impedances of Appendix 2 in this Guide

Where it is known that the actual operating temperature under normal load is less than the maximum permissible value for the type of cable insulation concerned (as given in the Tables of current-carrying capacity) the multipliers given in Table 6B may be reduced.

For verification purposes the designer will need to give the values of the phase and circuit protective conductor resistances at the ambient temperature expected during the tests. This may be different from the reference temperature of 20°C used for Table 6A. The following correction factors may be applied to the Table 6A values to take account of the ambient temperature (for test purposes only).

Expected ambient temperature	Correction factor
5°C	0.94
10°C	0.96
15°C	0.98
25°C	1.02

TABLE 6A

Value of resistance/metre for copper and aluminium conductors and of $R_1 + R_2$ per metre at 20°C in milliohms/metre

Cross-sectional area		Resistance/metre or $R_1 + R_2$/metre	
Phase Conductor	Protective Conductor	Plain Copper	Aluminium
1	—	18.10	
1	1	36.20	
1.5	—	12.10	
1.5	1	30.20	
1.5	1.5	24.20	
2.5	—	7.41	
2.5	1	25.51	
2.5	1.5	19.51	
2.5	2.5	14.82	
4	—	4.61	
4	1.5	16.71	
4	2.5	12.02	
4	4	9.22	
6	—	3.08	
6	2.5	10.49	
6	4	7.69	
6	6	6.16	
10	—	1.83	
10	4	6.44	
10	6	4.91	
10	10	3.66	
16	—	1.15	1.91
16	6	4.23	—
16	10	2.98	—
16	16	2.30	3.82
25	—	0.727	1.2
25	10	2.557	—
25	16	1.877	—
25	25	1.454	2.4
35	—	0.524	0.868
35	16	1.674	2.778
35	25	1.251	2.068
35	35	1.048	1.736

TABLE 6B

Multipliers to be applied to Table 6A

Insulation Material		p.v.c.	85°C rubber	90°C thermosetting
Multiplier	54B	1.30	1.42	1.48
	54C	1.38	1.53	1.60

The multipliers given in Table 6B are based on the simplified formula given in BS 6360 for both copper and aluminium conductors namely that the resistance-temperature coefficient is 0.004 per °C at 20°C.

54B applies where the protective conductor is not incorporated or bunched with cables, or for bare protective conductors in contact with cable covering.

54C applies where the protective conductor is a core in a cable or is bunched with cables.

NOTES

APPENDIX 7

CURRENT-CARRYING

CAPACITIES

AND

VOLTAGE DROP

FOR

COPPER

CONDUCTORS

TABLE 7A1
Single-core p.v.c.-insulated cables, non-armoured, with or without sheath
(COPPER CONDUCTORS)

Ambient temperature: 30°C. Conductor operating temperature: 70°C

CURRENT-CARRYING CAPACITY (Amperes): BS 6004, BS 6231, BS 6346

Conductor cross-sectional area	Reference Method 4 (enclosed in conduit in thermally insulating wall etc)		Reference Method 3 (enclosed in conduit on a wall or in trunking etc)		Reference Method 1 (clipped direct)		Reference Method 11 (on a perforated cable tray horizontal or vertical)		Reference Method 12 (free air)		
	2 cables, single-phase a.c or d.c	3 or 4 cables three-phase a.c	2 cables, single-phase a.c or d.c	3 or 4 cables three-phase a.c	2 cables, single-phase a.c or d.c flat and touching	3 or 4 cables three-phase a.c flat and touching or trefoil	2 cables, single-phase a.c or d.c flat and touching	3 or 4 cables three-phase a.c flat and touching or trefoil	Horizontal flat spaced — 2 cables, single-phase a.c or d.c or 3 cables three-phase a.c	Vertical flat spaced — 2 cables, single-phase a.c or d.c or 3 cables three-phase a.c	Tre-foil — 3 cables tre-foil three-phase a.c
1	2	3	4	5	6	7	8	9	10	11	12
mm²	A	A	A	A	A	A	A	A	A	A	A
1	11	10.5	13.5	12	15.5	14	—	—	—	—	—
1.5	14.5	13.5	17.5	15.5	20	18	—	—	—	—	—
2.5	19.5	18	24	21	27	25	—	—	—	—	—
4	26	24	32	28	37	33	—	—	—	—	—
6	34	31	41	36	47	43	—	—	—	—	—
10	46	42	57	50	65	59	—	—	—	—	—
16	61	56	76	68	87	79	—	—	—	—	—
25	80	73	101	89	114	104	126	112	146	130	110
35	99	89	125	110	141	129	156	141	181	162	137
50	119	108	151	134	182	167	191	172	219	197	167
70	151	136	192	171	234	214	246	223	281	254	216
95	182	164	232	207	284	261	300	273	341	311	264

Note: Where the conductor is to be protected by a semi-enclosed fuse to BS 3036, see Item 6.2 of Preface to Appendix 4, 16th Edition. The current-carrying capacities in columns 2 to 5 are also applicable to flexible cables to BS 6004 Table 1(c) and to 85°C heat resisting p.v.c. cables to BS 6231 where the cables are used in fixed installations.

Table 7A1 continued on page 88

TABLE 7A2
Voltage drop (per ampere per metre):   Conductor operating temperature: 70°C

Conductor cross-sectional area (mm²)	2 cables d.c. (mV)	2 cables – single-phase a.c. Ref. Methods 3 & 4 (Enclosed in conduit etc in or on a wall)				2 cables – single-phase a.c. Ref. Methods 1 & 11 (Clipped direct or on trays, touching)				2 cables – single-phase a.c. Ref. Method 12 (Spaced*)				3 or 4 cables – three-phase a.c. Ref. Methods 3 & 4 (Enclosed in conduit etc in or on a wall)				3 or 4 cables – three-phase a.c. Ref. Methods 1, 11 & 12 (In trefoil)				3 or 4 cables – three-phase a.c. Ref. Methods 1 & 11 (Flat and touching)				3 or 4 cables – three-phase a.c. Ref. Method 12 (Flat spaced*)			
		mV	r	x	z	mV	r	x	z	mV	r	x	z	mV	r	x	z	mV	r	x	z	mV	r	x	z	mV	r	x	z
1	44	44				44				44				38				38				38				38			
1.5	29	29				29				29				25				25				25				25			
2.5	18	18				18				18				15				15				15				15			
4	11	11				11				11				9.5				9.5				9.5				9.5			
6	7.3	7.3				7.3				7.3				6.4				6.4				6.4				6.4			
10	4.4	4.4				4.4				4.4				3.8				3.8				3.8				3.8			
16	2.8	2.8				2.8				2.8				2.4				2.4				2.4				2.4			
25	1.75		1.80	0.33	1.80		1.75	0.20	1.75		1.75	0.29	1.80		1.50	0.29	1.55		1.50	0.175	1.50		1.50	0.25	1.55		1.50	0.82	1.55
35	1.25		1.30	0.31	1.30		1.25	0.195	1.25		1.25	0.28	1.30		1.10	0.27	1.10		1.10	0.170	1.10		1.10	0.24	1.10		1.10	0.32	1.15
50	0.93		0.95	0.30	1.00		0.93	0.190	0.95		0.93	0.28	0.97		0.81	0.26	0.85		0.80	0.165	0.82		0.80	0.24	0.84		0.80	0.32	0.86
70	0.63		0.65	0.29	0.72		0.63	0.185	0.66		0.63	0.27	0.69		0.56	0.25	0.61		0.55	0.160	0.57		0.55	0.24	0.60		0.40	0.31	0.51
95	0.46		0.49	0.28	0.56		0.47	0.180	0.50		0.47	0.27	0.54		0.42	0.24	0.48		0.41	0.155	0.43		0.41	0.23	0.47		0.32	0.30	0.44
120	0.36		0.39	0.27	0.47		0.37	0.175	0.41		0.37	0.26	0.45		0.33	0.23	0.41		0.32	0.150	0.36		0.32	0.23	0.40		0.26	0.30	0.40
150	0.29		0.31	0.27	0.41		0.30	0.175	0.34		0.29	0.26	0.39		0.27	0.23	0.36		0.26	0.150	0.30		0.26	0.23	0.34		0.21	0.30	0.36
185	0.23		0.25	0.27	0.37		0.24	0.170	0.29		0.24	0.26	0.35		0.22	0.23	0.32		0.21	0.145	0.26		0.21	0.22	0.31		0.160	0.29	0.34
240	0.180		0.195	0.26	0.33		0.185	0.165	0.25		0.185	0.25	0.31		0.17	0.23	0.29		0.160	0.145	0.22		0.160	0.22	0.27		0.130	0.29	0.32
300	0.145		0.160	0.26	0.31		0.150	0.165	0.22		0.150	0.25	0.29		0.14	0.23	0.27		0.130	0.140	0.190		0.130	0.22	0.25		0.100	0.29	0.31
400	0.105		0.130	0.26	0.29		0.120	0.160	0.20		0.115	0.25	0.27		0.12	0.22	0.25		0.105	0.140	0.175		0.105	0.21	0.24		0.081	0.29	0.30
500	0.086		0.110	0.26	0.28		0.098	0.155	0.185		0.093	0.24	0.26		0.10	0.22	0.25		0.086	0.135	0.160		0.086	0.21	0.23		0.066	0.28	0.30
630	0.068		0.094	0.25	0.27		0.081	0.155	0.175		0.076	0.24	0.25		0.08	0.22	0.24		0.072	0.135	0.150		0.072	0.21	0.22		0.053	0.28	0.29
800	0.053		—	—	—		0.068	0.150	0.165		0.061	0.24	0.25		—	—	—		0.060	0.130	0.145		0.060	0.21	0.22		0.044	0.28	0.29
1000	0.042		—	—	—		0.059	0.150	0.160		0.050	0.24	0.24		—	—	—		0.052	0.130	0.140		0.052	0.20	0.21				0.28

* *Note: Spacings larger than those specified in Reference Method 12 (See Table 4A) will result in larger voltage drop.*

TABLE 7A1
Single-core p.v.c.-insulated cables, non-armoured, with or without sheath
(COPPER CONDUCTORS)
Ambient temperature: 30°C. Conductor operating temperature: 70°C
CURRENT-CARRYING CAPACITY (Amperes): BS 6004, BS6231, BS6346

Conductor cross-sectional area	Reference Method 4 (enclosed in conduit in thermally insulating wall etc)		Reference Method 3 (enclosed in conduit on a wall or in trunking etc)		Reference Method 1 (clipped direct)		Reference Method 11 (on a perforated cable tray horizontal or vertical)		Reference Method 12 (free air)		
	2 cables, single-phase a.c or d.c	3 or 4 cables three-phase a.c	2 cables, single-phase a.c or d.c	3 or 4 cables three-phase a.c	2 cables, single-phase a.c or d.c flat and touching	3 or 4 cables three-phase a.c flat and touching or trefoil	2 cables, single-phase a.c or d.c flat and touching	3 or 4 cables three-phase a.c flat and touching or trefoil	Horizontal flat spaced — 2 cables, single-phase a.c or d.c or 3 cables three-phase a.c	Vertical flat spaced — 2 cables, single-phase a.c or d.c or 3 cables three-phase a.c	Tre-foil — 3 cables tre-foil three phase a.c
1	2	3	4	5	6	7	8	9	10	11	12
mm²	A	A	A	A	A	A	A	A	A	A	A
120	210	188	269	239	330	303	349	318	396	362	308
150	240	216	300	262	381	349	404	369	456	419	356
185	273	245	341	296	436	400	463	424	521	480	409
240	320	286	400	346	515	472	549	504	615	569	485
300	367	328	458	394	594	545	635	584	709	659	561
400	—	—	546	467	694	634	732	679	852	795	656
500	—	—	626	533	792	723	835	778	982	920	749
630	—	—	720	611	904	826	953	892	1138	1070	855
800	—	—	—	—	1030	943	1086	1020	1265	1188	971
1000	—	—	—	—	1154	1058	1216	1149	1420	1337	1079

Note: Where the conductor is to be protected by a semi-enclosed fuse to BS 3036, see Item 6.2 of Preface to Appendix 4, 16th Edition. The current-carrying capacities in columns 2 to 5 are also applicable to flexible cables to BS 6004 Table 1(c) and to 85°C heat resisting p.v.c. cables to BS 6231 where the cables are used in fixed installations.

TABLE 7A2
Voltage drop (per ampere per metre): Conductor operating temperature: 70°C

Conductor cross-sectional area (mm²) [1]	2 cables d.c. (mV) [2]	Ref Methods 3 & 4 (Enclosed in conduit etc in or on a wall) (mV) [3] r	x	z	Ref Methods 1 & 11 (Clipped direct or on trays, touching) (mV) [4] r	x	z	Ref Method 12 (Spaced*) (mV) [5] r	x	z	Ref Methods 3 & 4 (Enclosed in conduit etc in or on a wall) (mV) [6] r	x	z	Ref Methods 1, 11 & 12 (In trefoil) (mV) [7] r	x	z	Ref Methods 1 & 11 (Flat and touching) (mV) [8] r	x	z	Ref Method 12 (Flat spaced*) (mV) [9] r	x	z
			2 cables – single-phase a.c.										*3 or 4 cables – three-phase a.c.*									
1	44		44			44			44			38			38			38			38	
1.5	29		29			29			29			25			25			25			25	
2.5	18		18			18			18			15			15			15			15	
4	11		11			11			11			9.5			9.5			9.5			9.5	
6	7.3		7.3			7.3			7.3			6.4			6.4			6.4			6.4	
10	4.4		4.4			4.4			4.4			3.8			3.8			3.8			3.8	
16	2.8		2.8			2.8			2.8			2.4			2.4			2.4			2.4	
25	1.75	1.80	0.33	1.80	1.75	0.20	1.75	1.75	0.29	1.80	1.50	0.29	1.55	1.50	0.175	1.50	1.50	0.25	1.55	1.50	0.82	1.55
35	1.25	1.30	0.31	1.30	1.25	0.195	1.25	1.25	0.28	1.30	1.10	0.27	1.10	1.10	0.170	1.10	1.10	0.24	1.10	1.10	0.32	1.15
50	0.93	0.95	0.30	1.00	0.93	0.190	0.95	0.93	0.28	0.97	0.81	0.26	0.85	0.80	0.165	0.82	0.80	0.24	0.84	0.80	0.32	0.86
70	0.63	0.65	0.29	0.72	0.63	0.185	0.66	0.63	0.27	0.69	0.56	0.25	0.61	0.55	0.160	0.57	0.55	0.24	0.60	0.40	0.31	0.51
95	0.46	0.49	0.28	0.56	0.47	0.180	0.50	0.47	0.27	0.54	0.42	0.24	0.48	0.41	0.155	0.43	0.41	0.23	0.47			
120	0.36	0.39	0.27	0.47	0.37	0.175	0.41	0.37	0.26	0.45	0.33	0.23	0.41	0.32	0.150	0.36	0.32	0.23	0.40	0.32	0.30	0.44
150	0.29	0.31	0.27	0.41	0.30	0.175	0.34	0.29	0.26	0.39	0.27	0.23	0.36	0.26	0.150	0.30	0.26	0.23	0.34	0.26	0.30	0.40
185	0.23	0.25	0.27	0.37	0.24	0.170	0.29	0.24	0.26	0.35	0.22	0.23	0.32	0.21	0.145	0.26	0.21	0.22	0.31	0.21	0.30	0.36
240	0.180	0.195	0.26	0.33	0.185	0.165	0.25	0.185	0.25	0.31	0.17	0.23	0.29	0.160	0.145	0.22	0.160	0.22	0.27	0.160	0.29	0.34
300	0.145	0.160	0.26	0.31	0.150	0.165	0.22	0.150	0.25	0.29	0.14	0.23	0.27	0.130	0.140	0.190	0.130	0.22	0.25	0.130	0.29	0.32
400	0.105	0.130	0.26	0.29	0.120	0.160	0.20	0.115	0.25	0.27	0.12	0.22	0.25	0.105	0.140	0.175	0.105	0.21	0.24	0.100	0.29	0.31
500	0.086	0.110	0.26	0.28	0.098	0.155	0.185	0.093	0.24	0.26	0.10	0.22	0.25	0.086	0.135	0.160	0.086	0.21	0.23	0.081	0.29	0.30
630	0.068	0.094	0.25	0.27	0.081	0.155	0.175	0.076	0.24	0.25	0.08	0.22	0.24	0.072	0.135	0.150	0.072	0.21	0.22	0.066	0.28	0.29
800	0.053	—	—	—	0.068	0.150	0.165	0.061	0.24	0.25	—	—	—	0.060	0.130	0.145	0.060	0.21	0.22	0.053	0.28	0.29
1000	0.042	—	—	—	0.059	0.150	0.160	0.050	0.24	0.24	—	—	—	0.052	0.130	0.140	0.052	0.20	0.21	0.044	0.28	0.28

* Note: Spacings larger than those specified in Reference Method 12 (See Table 4A) will result in larger voltage drop.

89

TABLE 7B1
Multicore p.v.c.-insulatedcables, non-armoured (COPPER CONDUCTORS)
Ambient temperature: 30°C. Conductor operating temperature: 70°C
CURRENT-CARRYING CAPACITY (Amperes): BS 6004 BS 6346

Conductor cross-sectional area	Reference Method 4 (enclosed in an insulated wall, etc)		Reference Method 3 (enclosed in conduit on a wall or ceiling, or in trunking)		Reference Method 1 (clipped direct)		Reference Method 11 (on a perforated cable tray), or Reference Method 13 (free air)	
	1 two-core cable* single-phase a.c or d.c	1 three core cable* or 1 four-core cable, three-phase a.c	1 two-core cable*, or single-phase a.c or d.c	1 three-core cable* or 1 four-core cable, three-phase a.c	1 two-core cable* single-phase a.c or d.c	1 three-core cable* or 1 four-core cable, three-phase a.c	1 two-core cable*, single-phase a.c or d.c	1 three-core cable* or 1 four-core cable, three-phase a.c
mm²	2	3	4	5	6	7	8	9
1	A 11	A 10	A 13	A 11.5	A 15	A 13.5	A 17	A 14.5
1.5	14	13	16.5	15	19.5	17.5	22	18.5
2.5	18.5	17.5	23	20	27	24	30	25
4	25	23	30	27	36	32	40	34
6	32	29	38	34	46	41	51	43
10	43	39	52	46	63	57	70	60
16	57	52	69	62	85	76	94	80
25	75	68	90	80	112	96	119	101
35	92	83	111	99	138	119	148	126
50	110	99	133	118	168	144	180	153
70	139	125	168	149	213	184	232	196
95	167	150	201	179	258	223	282	238
120	192	172	232	206	299	259	328	276
150	219	196	258	225	344	299	379	319
185	248	223	294	255	392	341	434	364
240	291	261	344	297	461	403	514	430
300	344	298	394	339	530	464	539	497
400	—	—	470	402	634	557	715	597

* With or without protective conductor. Circular conductors are assumed for sizes up to and including 16mm. Values for larger sizes relate to shaped conductors and may safely be applied to circular conductors.

Note: Where the conductor is to be protected by a semi-enclosed fuse to BS 3036, see Item 6.2 of the Preface to Appendix 4, 16th Edition.

TABLE 7B2

Voltage drop: Conductor operating
(per ampere per metre):   temperature: 70°C

Conductor cross-sectional area 1	Two-core cable d.c 2	Two-core cable single-phase a.c 3			Three-or four-core cable three-phase a.c 4		
mm²	mV	mV			mV		
1	44	44			38		
1.5	29	29			25		
2.5	18	18			15		
4	11	11			9.5		
6	7.3	7.3			6.4		
10	4.4	4.4			3.8		
16	2.8	2.8			2.4		
		r	x	z	r	x	z
25	1.75	1.75	0.170	1.75	1.50	0.145	1.50
35	1.25	1.25	0.165	1.25	1.10	0.145	1.10
50	0.93	0.93	0.165	0.94	0.80	0.140	0.81
70	0.63	0.63	0.160	0.65	0.55	0.140	0.57
95	0.46	0.47	0.155	0.50	0.41	0.135	0.43
120	0.36	0.38	0.155	0.41	0.33	0.135	0.35
150	0.29	0.30	0.155	0.34	0.26	0.130	0.29
185	0.23	0.25	0.150	0.29	0.21	0.130	0.25
240	0.180	0.190	0.150	0.24	0.165	0.130	0.21
300	0.145	0.155	0.145	0.21	0.135	0.130	0.185
400	0.105	0.115	0.145	0.185	0.100	0.125	0.160

APPENDIX 8

FORMS OF COMPLETION AND INSPECTION CERTIFICATE

Introduction

(i) The forms of Completion, Inspection and Testing required by Part 7 of the Regulations shall be made out and signed by competent persons in respect of the design, construction, inspection and testing of the work.

(ii) Competent persons will, as appropriate to their function under i) above, have a sound knowledge and experience relevant to the nature of the installation undertaken and to the technical standards set down in the 16th Edition of the IEE Wiring Regulations, be fully versed in the inspection and testing procedures contained in the 16th Edition of the IEE Wiring Regulations and employ adequate testing equipment.

(iii) Completed forms will indicate the responsibility for design, construction, inspection and testing, whether in relation to new work or further work on an existing installation.

(iv) When making out and signing a form on behalf of a company or other business entity, individuals shall state for whom they are acting.

(v) Additional forms may be required as clarification, if needed by non technical persons, or in expansion, for larger or more complicated jobs.

FORMS OF COMPLETION AND INSPECTION CERTIFICATE

(as prescribed in the IEE Regulations for Electrical Installations)

(1.) (see Notes overleaf)

DETAILS OF THE INSTALLATION

Client: *Good Food Grocery Ltd*

Address: *34 High Street. All Town*

DESIGN

I/We being the person(s) responsible (as indicated by my/our signatures below) for the Design of the electrical installation, particulars of which are described on Page 3 of this form CERTIFY that the said work for which I/we have been responsible is to the best of my/our knowledge and belief in accordance with the Regulations for Electrical Installations published by the Institution of Electrical Engineers, 16th Edition, amended to (3.) (date . . . .) except for the departures, if any, stated in this Certificate.

The extent of liability of the signatory is limited to the work described above as the subject of this Certificate.

For the DESIGN of the installation:

Name (In Block Letters): *2. PLANNER*   Position: *Design Engineer*

For and on behalf of: *New Electrical Design Partners*

Address: *Surbiton*

(2.) Signature: *a. Planner.*   (3.) Date *20th September 1991*

CONSTRUCTION

I/We being the person(s) responsible (as indicated by my/our signatures below) for the Construction of the electrical installation, particulars of which are described on Page 3 of this form CERTIFY that the said work for which I/we have been responsible is to the best of my/our knowledge and belief in accordance with the Regulations for Electrical Installations published by the Institution of Electrical Engineers, 16th Edition, amended to (3.) (date . . . .) except for the departures, if any, stated in this Certificate.

The extent of liability of the signatory is limited to the work described above as the subject of this Certificate.

For the CONSTRUCTION of the installation:

Name (In Block Letters): *B. CONDUIT*   Position: *CONTRACTS ENGINEER*

For and on behalf of: *ALL TOWN ELECTRICS LTD*

Address: *LOWER STREET ALL TOWN*

(2.) Signature: *R. Conduit*   (3.) Date: *22nd SEPTEMBER 1991*

INSPECTION AND TEST

I/We being the person(s) responsible (as indicated by my/our signatures below) for the Inspection and Test of the electrical installation, particulars of which are described on Page 3 of this form CERTIFY that the said work for which I/we have been responsible is to the best of my/our knowledge and belief in accordance with the Regulations for Electrical Installations published by the Institution of Electrical Engineers, 16th Edition, amended on (3.) (date . . . .) except for departures, if any, stated in this Certificate.

The extent of liability of the signatory is limited to the work described above as the subject of this Certificate.

For the INSPECTION AND TEST of the installation:

Name (In Block Letters): *J. WORTH*   Position: *TECHNICIAN*

For and on behalf of: *ALLTOWN ELECTRICS LTD*

Address: *LOWER STREET ALLTOWN*

I RECOMMEND that this installation be further inspected and tested after an interval of not more than . *5* . years. (5.)

(2.) Signature: *J. Worth*   (3.) Date: *22nd September 1991*

(6) page 1 of . *4* . pages

93

1. This document is intended for the initial certification of a new installation or of an alteration or addition to an existing installation and of an inspection.

2. The signatures appended are those of the persons authorised by the companies executing the work of design, construction and inspection and testing respectively. A signatory authorised to certify more than one category of work shall sign in each of the appropriate places.

3. Dates to be inserted.

4. Where particulars of the installation recorded herein constitute a sufficient schedule for the purpose of Regulation 514-09-01 further drawings/schedules need not be provided. For other installations the additional drawings/schedules listed below apply.

5. Insert here the time interval recommended between periodic inspections. Regard should be paid to relevant national or local legislation and reference should be made to Chapter 13 of the 16th Edition of the IEE Wiring Regulations.

6. The page numbers of each sheet should be indicated together with the total number of sheets involved.

Printed copies of this Completion and Inspection Certificate cannot be obtained from the Institution. There is no objection to its reproduction providing its source, the Institution of Electrical Engineers, is acknowledged.

(4) Schedule of additional records.

Page 2 of 4 Pages.

94

PARTICULARS OF THE INSTALLATION

(Delete or complete items as appropriate)

Type of Installation   New/alteration/addition/to existing installation

Type of Earthing (312-03):
(Indicate in the box)

TN-C	TN-S	TN-C-S	TT	IT
☐	☐	✓	☐	☐

Earth Electrode: Resistance ..... N/A .... ohms

Method of Measurement ....

Type (542-02-01) and Location ....

Characteristics of the supply at the origin of the installation (313-01):

Nominal voltage .... 240 .... volts

Frequency .... 50 .... Hz

Number of phases .. 3 .....

Prospective short-circuit current .... 1.2 .... kA

Earth fault loop impedance (Z_s) ...... 0.2 ...... ohms

	ascertained by enquiry	determined by calculation	measured
			✓
			✓

Maximum demand ....A per phase

Overcurrent protective device - Type BS 1361 $Type2$ Rating 100 A

Main switch or circuit breaker (460-01-02): Type BS .... Rating 100 A No of poles 3

(if an r.c.d., rated residual operating current $I_{\Delta n}$ .... mA.)

Method of protection against indirect contact:

1. Earthed equipotential bonding and automatic disconnection of supply ✓

or

2. Other ☐ (Describe) ....

Main equipotential bonding conductors (413-02-01/02, 547-02-01): Size.... 10 ... mm²

Schedule of Test Results: Continuation .... 1 ...... pages

Details of departures (if any) from the Wiring Regulations (120-04, 120-05).... $NONE$ ....

Comments on existing installation, where applicable (743-01-01): ...... N/A ......

(6) page 3 of 4 pages

INSTALLATION SCHEDULE

Type of Supply TN-C-S
Z₀ at origin .O.2. ohms → Z_e at origin .O.2. ohms
PSSC .....l..2... kA

Property SHOP
34 HIGH STREET
ALLTOWN

Contractor

Test Date 22-9-91
Inspection by J. WORTH
Signature J. Worth

Instruments:
rcd tester .7/.0.436
e/loop .A.21.444
continuity M/3A43
insulation M/3A43
others ....
....

Description of work completed . REWIRE SHOP. 3 PHASE DIS. BOARD ....

Distribution Board	no. of points	Fuse /acb type	Rating amps	Cable size mm²	length m	CPC mm²	Z_e Ω	Ins Res MΩ	Polarity	RCD mS	Ring Cont	Remarks
1. FRONT LIGHTS	6	2	5	1.5	15	1.0	0.5	10	✓	–	–	
2. REAR LIGHTS	7	2	5	1.5	25	1.0	0.75	10	✓	–	–	
3. SOCKETS LMS	6 TWIN	2	30	2.5	22	1.5	0.32	15	✓	15	–	
4. SOCKETS RMS	6 TWIN	2	30	2.5	28	1.5	0.35	15	✓	20	–	
5. SPUR TO KITCHEN	2 TWIN	2	30	4.0	30	2.5	0.45	10	✓	–	–	
6.)												
7.) FREEZER 1	ONE	3	10	2.5	20	2.5	0.51	20+	✓	–	–	4 CORE SWA CABLE
8.) 3 PHASE												
9.)												
10.) FREEZER 2	ONE	3	10	2.5	10	2.5	0.35	20+	✓	–	–	4 CORE SWA CABLE
11.) 3 PHASE												
12. WATER HEATER	ONE	2		2.5	25	1.5	0.7	10	✓			

(Note Z_e shown as measured at outlet or point.)

Main bonding check: Gas ✓ Water ✓ Other OIL ✓

Deviations from Wiring Regulations and special notes: NOTE:
DISCONNECT LIGHTING (ELECTRONIC BALLASTS) BEFORE TESTING AND UNPLUG
TILLS.

Page 4 of 4 page

APPENDIX 9
CONVENTIONAL CIRCUIT ARRANGEMENT

This Appendix gives details of conventional circuit arrangements which satisfy the requirements of Chapter 43 of the 16th Edition of the IEE Wiring Regulations for overload protection and, similarly, Chapter 46 for isolation and switching, together with the requirements as regards current-carrying capacities of conductors prescribed in Chapter 52 (Cables, conductors and wiring materials).

It is the responsibility of the designer and installer when adopting these circuit arrangements to take the appropriate measures to comply with the requirements of other Chapters or Sections which are relevant, such as Chapter 41 (Protection against electric shock), Section 434 (Protection against fault current), Chapter 54 (Earthing and protective conductors), and the requirements of Chapter 52 other than those concerning current-carrying capacities.

Circuit arrangements other than those detailed in this Appendix are not precluded where they are specified by a suitably qualified electrical engineer, in accordance with the general requirements of Regulation 314-01-03.

The conventional circuit arrangements are:

— Final circuits using socket-outlets complying with BS 1363

— Final circuits using socket-outlets complying with BS 196

— Final radial circuits using socket-outlets complying with BS 4343

— Cooker final circuits in household premises.

Final circuits using socket-outlets complying with BS 1361 and fused connection units

General

A ring or radial circuit, with spurs if any, feeds permanently connected equipment and an unlimited number of socket-outlets.

The floor area served by the circuit is determined by the known or estimated load but does not exceed the value given in Table 9A.

For household installations a single 30 A ring circuit may serve a floor area of up to 100 m² but consideration should be given to the loading in kitchens which may require a separate circuit. For other types of premises, final circuits complying with Table 9A may be installed where, owing to diversity, the maximum demand of current-using equipment to be connected is estimated not to exceed the corresponding ratings of the overcurrent protective device given in that table.

The number of socket-outlets is such as to ensure compliance with Regulation 553-01-07, each socket-outlet of a twin or multiple socket-outlet unit being regarded as one socket-outlet.

Diversity between socket-outlets and permanently connected equipment has already been taken into account in Table 9A and no further diversity should be applied.

TABLE 9A

Final circuits using BS 1363 socket-outlets

			Minimum conductor size*		
Type of circuit	Overcurrent protective device		Copper conductor rubber-or p.v.c.-insulated cables	Copper conductor mineral-insulated cables	Maximum floor area served
1	Rating 2	Type 3	4	6	7
A1 Ring	A 30 or 32	Any	mm² 2.5	mm² 1.5	m² 100
A2 Radial	30 or 32	Cartridge fuse or circuit breaker	4	2.5	50
A3 Radial	20	Any	2.5	1.5	20

* The tabulated values of conductor size may be reduced for fused spurs

Immersion heaters, fitted to storage vessels in excess of 15 litres capacity, or permanently connected heating appliances forming part of a comprehensive space heating installation are supplied by their own separate circuits.

Where two or more ring final circuits are installed the socket-outlets and permanently connected equipment to be served are reasonably distributed among the circuits.

Circuit protection

The overcurrent protective device is of the type, and has the rating, given in Table 9A.

Conductor size

The minimum size of conductor in the circuit and in non-fused spurs is given in Table 9A. However, if the cables of more than two circuits are bunched together or the ambient temperature exceeds 30°C, the size of conductor is increased and is determined by applying the appropriate correction factors from Appendix 7, so that the conductor size then corresponds to a current-carrying capacity not less than:

(i)   20 A for circuit A1 (i.e. 0.67 times the rating of the overcurrent protective device).

(ii)   30 A or 32 A for circuit A2 (i.e. the rating of the overcurrent protective device).

(iii) 20 A for circuit A3 (i.e. the rating of the overcurrent protective device).

The conductor size for a fused spur is determined from the total current demand served by that spur, which is limited to a maximum of 13 A.

(iv) when such a spur serves socket-outlets the minimum conductor size is:

(a) 1.5 mm² for rubber- or p.v.c.-insulated cables, copper conductors

(b) 2.5 mm² for rubber- or p.v.c.-insulated cables, copper-clad aluminium conductors.

(c) 1 mm² for mineral-insulated cables, copper conductors.

Spurs

The total number of fused spurs is unlimited but the number of non-fused spurs does not exceed the total number of socket-outlets and items of stationary equipment connected directly in the circuit.

A non-fused spur feeds only one single or one twin socket-outlet or one permanently connected equipment. Such a spur is connected to a circuit at the terminals of socket-outlets or at joint boxes or at the origin of the circuit in the distribution board.

A fused spur is connected to the circuit through a fused connection unit, the rating of the fuse in the unit not exceeding that of the cable forming the spur, and, in any event, not exceeding 13 A.

Permanently connected equipment

Permanently connected equipment is locally protected by a fuse of rating not exceeding 13 A and controlled by a switch conforming with the requirements of Chapter 46, or protected by a circuit-breaker of rating not exceeding 16 A.

Final circuit using socket-outlets complying with BS 196

General

A ring or radial circuit, with fused spurs if any, feeds equipment the maximum demand of which, having allowed for diversity, is known or estimated not to exceed the rating of the overcurrent protective device and in any event does not exceed 32 A.

In assessing the maximum demand it is assumed that permanently connected equipment operates continuously, i.e., no diversity is allowed in respect of such equipment.

The number of socket-outlets is unlimited.

The total current demand of points served by a fused spur does not exceed 16 A.

Circuit protection

The overcurrent protective device has a rating not exceeding 32 A.

Conductor size

The size of conductor is determined by applying from Appendix 4 of the Regulations the appropriate correction factors and is such that it then corresponds to a current-carrying capacity of:

(i) for ring circuits—not less than 0.67 times the rating of the overcurrent protective device.

(ii) for radial circuits—not less than the rating of the overcurrent protective device.

The conductor size for a fused spur is determined from the total demand served by that spur which is limited to a maximum of 16 A.

Spurs

A fused spur is connected to a circuit through a fused connection unit, the rating of the fuse in the unit not exceeding that of the cable forming the spur and in any event not exceeding 16 A.

Non-fused spurs are not used.

Permanently connected equipment

Permanently connected equipment is locally protected by a fuse of rating not exceeding 16 A and controlled by a switch conforming with the requirements of Chapter 46 or by a circuit-breaker of rating not exceeding 16 A.

Types of socket-outlets

If the circuit has one pole earthed, the socket-outlet is to be of the type that will accept only 2-pole-and-earth contact plugs with single-pole fusing on the live pole. Such socket-outlets are those which have raised socket keys to prevent insertion of non-fused plugs, together with socket keyways recessed at position 'B' and such other positions as are specified in the British Standard according to the nature of the supply to the socket-outlets.

If the circuit has neither pole earthed (e.g. a circuit supplied from a double-wound transformer having the mid-point of its secondary winding earthed) the socket-outlet is to be the type that will accept only 2-pole-and-earth contact plugs with double-pole fusing. Such socket-outlets are those which have raised socket keys to prevent insertion of non-fused plugs, together with socket keyways recessed at position 'P' and such other positions as are specified in the British Standard according to the nature of the supply to the socket-outlets.

Final radial circuits using 16 A socket-outlets complying with BS 4343

General

Where a radial circuit feeds equipment the maximum demand of which, having allowed for diversity, is known or estimated not to exceed the rating of the overcurrent protective device and in any event does not exceed 20 A.

The number of socket-outlets is unlimited.

Circuit protection

The overcurrent protective device is to have a rating not exceeding 20 A.

Conductor size

The size of conductor is determined by applying from Appendix 4 of the Regulations the appropriate correction factors and is such that it then corresponds to a current-carrying capacity not less than the rating of the overcurrent protective device.

Types of socket-outlets

Socket-outlets should have a rated current of 16 A and be of the type appropriate to the number of phases, circuit voltage and earthing arrangement. Socket-outlets incorporating pilot contacts are not included.

Cooker circuits in household premises

The circuit supplies a control switch or a cooker unit which may incorporate a socket-outlet.

The rating of the circuit is determined by the assessment of the current demand of the cooking appliance(s), and control unit socket-outlet if any, in accordance with Table 1A.

A circuit of rating exceeding 15 A but not exceeding 50 A may supply two or more cooking appliances where these are installed in one room. The control switch should be placed within two metres of the appliance. Where two stationary cooking appliances are installed in one room, one switch may be used to control both appliances provided that neither appliance is more than two metres from the switch.

Attention is drawn to the need to afford discriminative operation of protective gear as stated in Regulation 533-01-06.

NOTES

ON-SITE GUIDE   **ARRANGEMENT OF THE ORIGIN**

isolation and
switching 5
functional
switching 5.2
isolation 5.1(iii)

emergency
switch 5.4

labelling 6.1(v)

labelling 6.1(i)
and (ii) unexpected
voltage exceeding
240v

labelling 6.1(iii)
presence of
different nominal
voltages

DATA

fireman's emergency
switch 5.4

neon sign

external equipment
IP code, 8.2.1(iv)

EMMA

category 3
circuit 9.2.2(x)

garage
or shed

particular
attention is
required
8.2.1

conventional
final circuits
table 7.1
assumed
conditions
7.1

choice of
protective devices
7.2.4

bathrooms and
showers 8

disconnection
times, special
circuits 3.5.2

104

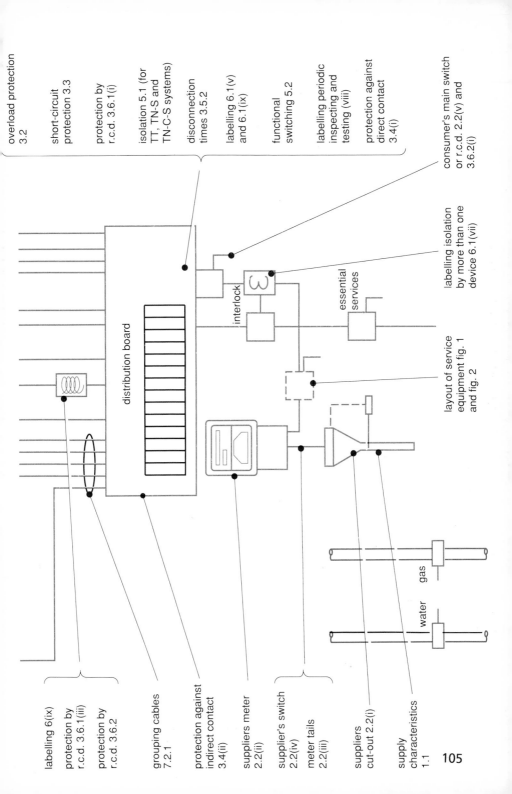

overload protection 3.2

short-circuit protection 3.3

protection by r.c.d. 3.6.1(i)

isolation 5.1 (for TT, TN-S and TN-C-S systems)

disconnection times 3.5.2

labelling 6.1(v) and 6.1(ix)

functional switching 5.2

labelling periodic inspecting and testing (viii)

protection against direct contact 3.4(i)

consumer's main switch or r.c.d. 2.2(v) and 3.6.2(i)

labelling isolation by more than one device 6.1(vii)

essential services

interlock

distribution board

layout of service equipment fig. 1 and fig. 2

water   gas

labelling 6(ix)

protection by r.c.d. 3.6.1(iii)

protection by r.c.d. 3.6.2

grouping cables 7.2.1

protection against indirect contact 3.4(ii)

suppliers meter 2.2(ii)

supplier's switch 2.2(iv)

meter tails 2.2(iii)

suppliers cut-out 2.2(i)

supply characteristics 1.1

105

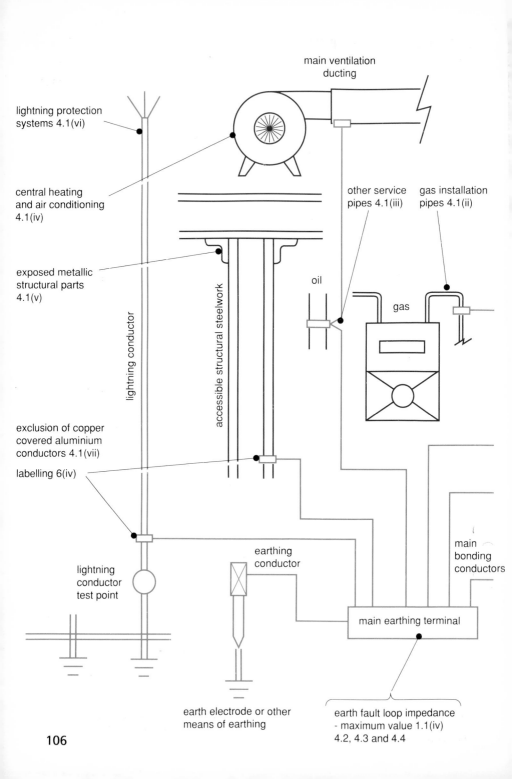

main ventilation
ducting

lightning protection
systems 4.1(vi)

central heating
and air conditioning
4.1(iv)

other service
pipes 4.1(iii)

gas installation
pipes 4.1(ii)

exposed metallic
structural parts
4.1(v)

oil

gas

lightning conductor

accessible structural steelwork

exclusion of copper
covered aluminium
conductors 4.1(vii)

labelling 6(iv)

lightning
conductor
test point

earthing
conductor

main
bonding
conductors

main earthing terminal

earth electrode or other
means of earthing

earth fault loop impedance
- maximum value 1.1(iv)
4.2, 4.3 and 4.4

106

BONDING AND EARTHING
SEE ALSO FIGS (3), (4) AND (5)

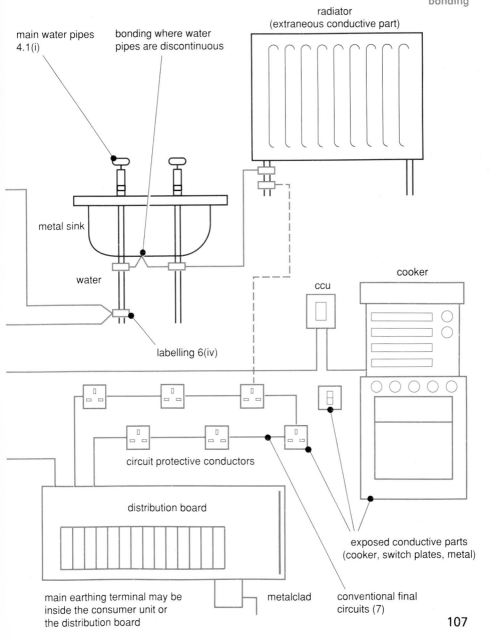

radiator
(extraneous conductive part)

main water pipes
4.1(i)

bonding where water
pipes are discontinuous

metal sink

water

cooker

ccu

labelling 6(iv)

circuit protective conductors

distribution board

exposed conductive parts
(cooker, switch plates, metal)

main earthing terminal may be
inside the consumer unit or
the distribution board

metalclad

conventional final
circuits (7)

107

SPECIAL LOCATIONS AND R.C.DS.

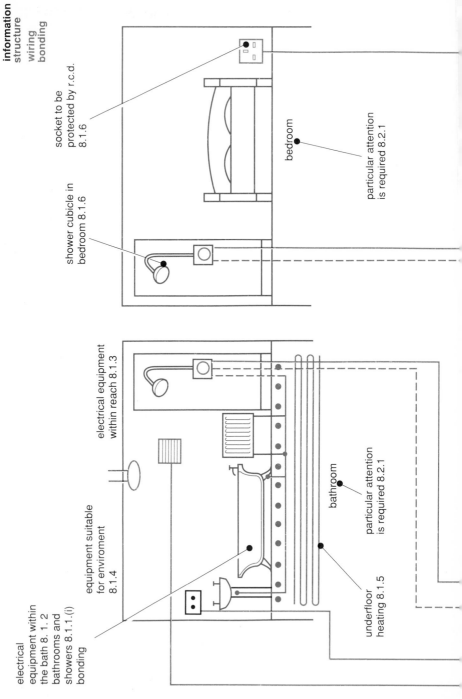

socket to be
protected by r.c.d.
8.1.6

shower cubicle in
bedroom 8.1.6

bedroom

particular attention
is required 8.2.1

electrical equipment
within reach 8.1.3

electrical
equipment within
the bath 8. 1. 2
bathrooms and
showers 8.1.1.(i)
bonding

equipment suitable
for enviroment
8.1.4

bathroom

particular attention
is required 8.2.1

underfloor
heating 8.1.5

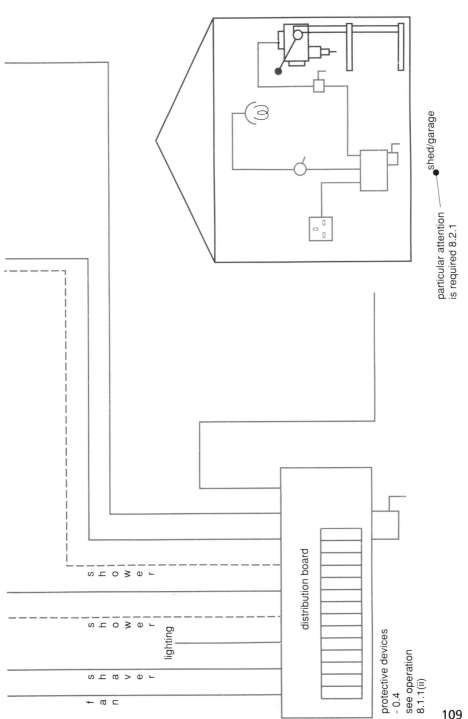

shed/garage

particular attention
is required 8.2.1

shower

shower

lighting

shaver

fan

distribution board

protective devices
- 0.4
see operation
8.1.1(ii)

109

INSPECTION AND TESTING

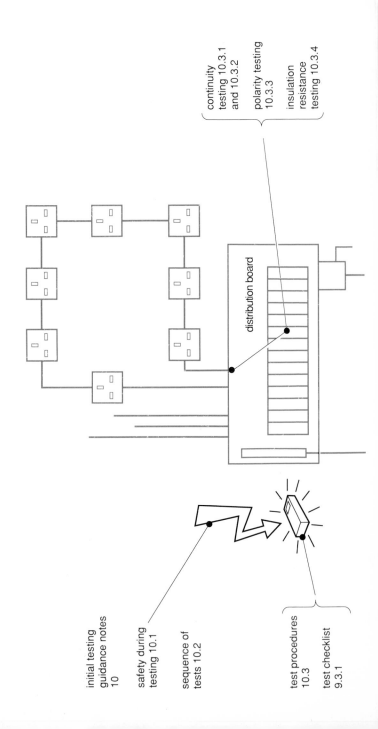

continuity
testing 10.3.1
and 10.3.2

polarity testing
10.3.3

insulation
resistance
testing 10.3.4

distribution board

initial testing
guidance notes
10

safety during
testing 10.1

sequence of
tests 10.2

test procedures
10.3

test checklist
9.3.1

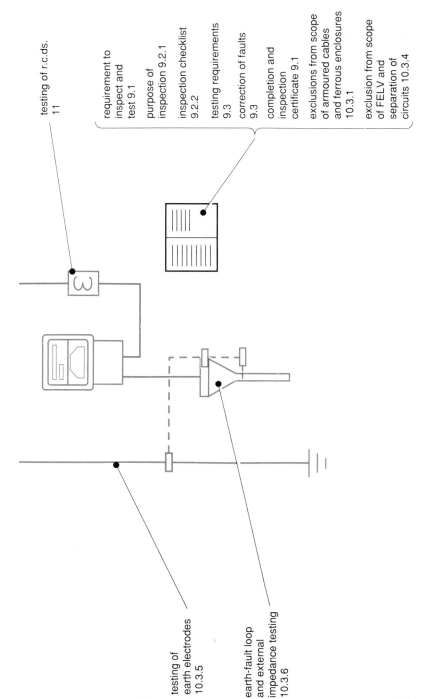

testing of r.c.ds. 11

requirement to inspect and test 9.1

purpose of inspection 9.2.1

inspection checklist 9.2.2

testing requirements 9.3

correction of faults 9.3

completion and inspection certificate 9.1

exclusions from scope of armoured cables and ferrous enclosures 10.3.1

exclusion from scope of FELV and separation of circuits 10.3.4

testing of earth electrodes 10.3.5

earth-fault loop and external impedance testing 10.3.6

NOTES